BEFORE
I
WON

Tomas Veres

FIRST EDITION

Cover design: Tomas Veres
Translation: Miriam Oravcova

www.tomasveres.com

instagram.com/tomasveres_

goodreads.com/tomasveres

ISBN 978-80-973115-0-6

To all of us that work hard, believe in ourselves
and in a better future.
Despite our families, friends and people around us shouting:
what the f*ck are you doing?

If you can imagine these things, and bond with them,
I would be honored.

And if you say afterwards,
"if Tom did it, I'll can do it too,"
you will be rewarded.

The decisions you made yesterday have brought you to the place where you are today. The decisions to be made today will bring you to a different place tomorrow. Please, share with us all the decisions from your past.

Some of us hope to make it to heaven after death. Some of us help the poor and believe that God will reward them. But as soon as I was born, and I found myself immediately in hell. I didn't get the opportunity to make something right or even to do something terrible, and look, I was already being punished. Thanks to my parents. Everything started when my mother met one guy. Then, one year later, something happened. A child named Tom Seed was born. Not as a star but as another useless piece of trash in this society.

My first days in the Montefiore Medical Center hospital were delightful. The same goes for the other newborns. I was the star for all the nurses with my green eyes and short curly blond hair. My small mouth was not able to talk yet. My weak body was not able to make any move. In spite of this, I was the one who created smiles on the faces of others. But I did not get to enjoy that pleasant place for a long time – my days in maternity hospital came to an end, and I had to go home as a healthy child with perfect parents. To a small apartment in the Bronx. The place that became my home. The place where we lived together as a real family. My mother spent entire days with me, while my father worked as parking lot attendant at a shopping mall. I had no toys to play with, but I was happy even without them because I had a loving mom who played with me all day long.

As life went on, I started to understand many things. I said my first words, took my first steps, hid my first teeth under my pillow. For me, big successes, for my parents, big issues. They didn't see me grow up – they just saw me ruining their lives and their furniture.

I never heard words like "I love you," "thank you," or "you are my hero"...

Instead I heard words, bad words... "you can't do anything," "you are the biggest mistake of my life," "even the dog's smarter than you"...

My parents shouting, that was my daily life. My mom shouted at me during the day, and in the night when dad came back from work, she shouted at him. At first I felt terrible. All the noise, all the shouting scared me. But after some time, I got used to it. I started to behave exactly like they did. I started to scream and shout like they did. I started to use the words they used. I thought it was correct, it was right to be the same as my parents. Until I started at nursery school.

That was the moment that changed everything.

M y teacher held my tiny hand, took my little bag and led me away from my mother. She held my hand so strongly that she almost broke it. I did not like it at all, I wanted to stay with my mom, but she moved away, further away from me. So, I shouted. Again and again. The other children looked at me like I was a monster they had never seen before. And all of a sudden, this lady, the one who would be my teacher, hit me so hard that it made me cry.

Very painful for me, but very funny for the other kids in nursery school. Even though I stopped crying after a couple of minutes, the children laughed the whole day. Nobody took care of me …

Nobody talked to me …

Nobody …

As I sat in the classroom, encircled by nothing, I heard something that made me happy again. The most important person in my life was back. My mom. She hadn't forgotten me. Finally, I was able to leave that place and never come back. On the way home, we stopped for groceries and my mom bought me a cherry flavor lollipop. I really enjoyed it, but I started to feel that something was going on, because up to that point I never got any sweets from my mom. Nothing.

This was not the only unusual thing to happen to me that day. The same bag I had with me in nursery school earlier was on the kitchen stool, ready for the next day. Curious, I asked my mom where we were going tomorrow. She told me that for the next couple of years, I'll be going to that nursery school every day like all the normal children my age.

My body was as paralyzed like a tree, while my eyes started tearing up like the sea.

I couldn't believe it. I wasn't able to accept it. I started to shout at my mom exactly like she did to my father when he comes back from work at night. But my beloved mom did something I never expected her to do. She started to pull my hair and hit me on the head. Stronger and stronger. Until I lost consciousness. I woke up only the next morning with bruises all over my body. It took me a while to realize what had happened. I wanted to say sorry to my mom, because I obviously had done something to her, otherwise she would never hit me that hard. I looked for her in every room, but I was notable to find her anywhere. She had left the apartment.

I didn't want to see my mom so upset. So I dressed, brushed my teeth, took my bag and did precisely what I had to do – I went to nursery school. I walked alone, completely scared of the outside world going on around me. On the way there I met a lot of weird people, heard many weird words and felt many weird smells. I thought my first day in nursery school was the worst. Unfortunately, I was wrong. The next days were even worse, much worse... Despite my fights with bullies, I still had to go. If I didn't do it, my mom would beat me at home.

My parents had no friends. They avoided people, and I inherited the same attitude towards people. I prefer solitude. In my class there were twenty-two students, and none of them played with me – there were some exceptions, but they also played an unfair game called bullying. I remember the day when I ended up in the hospital with cracked head because of them.

I also remember the day when the cops brought me home in a police cruiser because somebody hid my shoes and I had to walk home barefoot, with no shoes. My body suffered, my soul cried. I felt so lonely. I did not have anybody to play with and spend time with. So I took pencils and paper from off of the table, tilted my head down and left formy favorite place, the dark cold corner of my classroom. I closed my eyes for a couple of minutes, and then it happened. In front of me I saw beautiful objects. I started to draw everything I saw in my mind.

The children I was so scared of before because they were much older and stronger than me, they all became part of my drawings. This was the only way to escape reality. When I drew, I drew for entire days because when I held the pencil in my hand,there was no darkness in my head any more.

I saw the beauty in my drawings, but my parents saw only the costs connected to drawing. As a poor family we were not able to afford many things. Things like paper or pencils.

I would try anything, cry, beg, dream …

Nothing worked.

My parents simply did not have any money to spend on this. But one small act changed the whole situation. I stole a set of pencils and papers from nursery school so I could draw at home.

After I started elementary school, many things changed. A new building, new teachers, new classmates. Only one thing was still the same. I was a weirdo and this caused me a lot of issues. My nose was broken twice and my hand once. Later, I started to have problems with my grades. In the classroom, I was "the best." I had to learn things from history, literature and other stupid things. I hated it. I honestly believed that my life was jinxed.

I had no nanny, no adult supervision. My one and only companion was an old television in the kitchen. At school I listened to boring stories about Abraham Lincoln, but at home I watched exciting stories about Pablo Escobar on TV, about the violence taking place in my surroundings. In the world-famous Bronx.

I didn't want to be asweet boy in suit just like Abraham Lincoln. I wanted to be that tough guy, like Pablo Escobar and his companions were, with guns in the streets. I watched TV late at night because that was the only time when I could watch gangster movies. I loved them. I liked them so much that I decided to skip school. As my mom and dad worked long hours, I watched television. It didn't take long for my parents to realize something was wrong. The electricity bills were much higher than usual, but my parents also got a letter. A letter from my school with news about my absence. It took only a couple of minutes for my body to change color. They beat me.

Then they told me that we're not wealthy people. We're poor people because rich people and their families are thieves. That's why they have so much money. They stole it.

I understood why my parents beat me, but I did not understand why rich people should be so bad. Why, if they have that much money, do they not support people like me? You know. My family did not own any car, we could only afford good meat on Christmas Eve, I wore old clothes that didn't fit me.

And them?

They own luxury European cars, live in private suburbs, wear silk clothes and eat healthy and fresh meals every day.

At the age of fifteen I discovered who had jinxed my life. Rich people! They jinxed my life and my parents' lives. They have their own TV shows where they pay thousands and thousands of dollars for their children's birthday parties. They buy gold-decorated houses for their tiny dogs, bigger than my room. They are popular while people like me, the poor people of the Bronx, are hated because the world sees us only as criminal animals on the news. Life in the Bronx is tough, my father often said. I understood what he meant. The whole time I lived in the Bronx, I've only seen a few rich people. Everybody knew well that the wealthy people live in Manhattan.

In a place filled with stars and luxury. A place just a mile away from our apartment. I couldn't concentrate, I was still thinking about the people in Manhattan enjoying life in luxury, and I became determined to get my revenge. Immediately I went to the bus stop and hopped on to the nearest bus to Manhattan.

When I got there, I felt like I was in another world. Huge modern buildings, clean streets, shops with glass windows. Everyone wore noble clothes with an unidentifiable scent … Gold watches shone on their wrists …

They all looked so happy there.

In this world, young people bow their heads as they played games on their phones, but in my world, young people bowed their heads because the color of their eyes showed which drugs they'd been using.

In this world, the people embraced each other on benches because they were in love. People in my world held each other because they had to keep warm.

In this world, people were walking fast because they were hurrying home to their perfect families, while in my world, people walked fast because they had just witnessed a crime.

Not a reality show on TV. Only reality. I took a deep breath and I joined the people around me. They looked kind, everyone was smiling at each other. I wanted to be loved, I wanted to be happy, I wanted to be part of that perfect world even for just a few seconds. I only needed a few seconds …

As usual, something went wrong. The people around me who looked happy just a few moments ago with wide smiles on their faces weren't saying anything. They just walked like statues. No joy, no smiles. Then I remembered. I remembered where I saw the same expression they were wearing on their faces. The same expression the kids in the nursery school had when they looked at me like a screaming monster. I didn't need to see any more. It was enough to prove the point.

I didn't go home. I stayed there until night, when all the people went to sleep in their luxury apartments. Then, my revenge began. It was so easy. When I saw a fancy car parked along the street, I took my apartment keys and scratched it. Repeatedly. I had a great feeling after that. I had a great feeling about myself. That night I keyed more than fifteen cars.

I felt like a real gangster, a boy who belonged to the victims of violence, who had himself become part of the violence.

After a few days, I had the urge to do it again. But this time with a greater effect. I couldn't just sit so idly at home. I had to create something out of the hatred that I felt within myself. I decided to do it on a Sunday, because it does not matter what color you are, how old you are, where you live or how much money you have, all people were gathered in one place –at church.

I put only two things in my bag: a knife and spray paint. I chose the same target. Luxury cars in Manhattan parked along the street. With my mom's kitchen knife I cut all four wheels on each car. With blue paint I sprayed the message:

"Thief!" I wanted to see the car owners' expressions when they woke up in the morning and see the surprise I had prepared for them. I didn't have to wait until morning. I just closed my eyes and imagined it. I enjoyed it. Until I heard a male voice shouting from a nearby street.

My heart was beating like crazy. I panicked. I started to run away. I ran as fast as I could. I could not stop. I was frightened that the guy would catch me in the act and call the police. I have no clue how, but I made it home from there. It was probably a miracle that I got home. When my adrenaline disappeared, I began to regret my act.

The fear of being discovered was stronger than the joy of revenge. I tried to forget that night, but I could not. From that moment on, I asked God for forgiveness. I promised myself that I would never do anything like that again. The next morning I went to school like usual. The same way, the same people. But things I had never noticed before started to make me mad. Car sounds, police sirens, the clock ticking, laughter …

All these everyday things made me angry. I was afraid, and fear was destroying me. I avoided all eye contact. I stopped eating. I felt terrible.

My mind was filled with the horrible feeling of having a conscience. I was down in the dumps.

I picked up a knife from the dining room, and I went to the bathroom and locked myself in.

There, in that bathroom, I wanted to end my suffering, but I couldn't do it.

I was so weak …

So weak …

I was just lying there on the dirty floor like an old ship wreck on the shore, crying.

I cried till I could see a white light.

God had listened to me,

God had heard my prayers …

Or so I thought.

Apparently, I hadn't seen the same light that people see just before death. The light I saw was coming from the flashlight of an NYPD Police Officer.

The vandal who had scratched thirty-six cars in Manhattan ended in a juvenile detention. "A young man from the Bronx who listened to too many 50 Cent songs," wrote a New York Post journalist.

As I later realized from that police officer, at the crime scene, they found a book that had fallen out of my bag during my bloody escape. Also, images from security cameras recorded my act. The police had clear evidence of my guilt. I knew it, they knew it, they all knew it. After a few hours spent in the juvenile detention, they led me to a judge with deep wrinkles on his face. I stood before him as a dangerous criminal, waiting for my punishment.

Dear young man – the judge said, *your acts reflect your thoughts, and people who cannot control their thoughts are in prison or on the way there. Now I'll give you a chance to turn it around, to change your life. Remember this, because you will not get a second chance.*

The judge stood up, picked up the gavel, hit it on a large table and said his verdict. I was let free. He hadn't lied to me. I really was given a second chance.

I could finally sleep peacefully. My secrets had been revealed. I didn't have to worry about it anymore. I didn't have to hide it anymore within myself. I felt a huge sense of relief. It literally set me free. It helped me.

Unfortunately, someone else was hurt by it. My parents were worried. I had let them down big time. I did not hear any words coming from them. I didn't have to.

I saw the shame, the pain in their eyes.

What happened, happened. I was sorry. Two days later I received a diploma for successfully completing elementary school together with a detailed report on the condition of my release set by the New York City Court. The terms: another offense would be considered as a criminal offense without the possibility for dismissal.

It took more than ten days for my parents to start talking to me. They had to, because we had a guest. It was the first time someone else had come to our old apartment. We never had a guest at home. A man came wearing a blue suit and bright red tie. Or in other words: a Manhattan lawyer wearing a blue suit and bright red tie that represented the wealthy owners of the damaged cars.

He closely reviewed our modestly furnished apartment, which looked amazing in his words, he asked us how we were doing, and then he showed us papers from the insurance company. He explained to us that even if I damaged the cars, the insurance company would pay all the costs associated with the repairs.

A very nice message for me and my parents. The lawyer wished me a lot of luck, shook my hand and left. There was only the strong cinnamon scent of his perfume left after that. It could not have gone better. I hadn't caused any problems for my family. We could go back to how things were before.

The punishment I received was more like a reward.

I got sentenced to two months house arrest. That meant for me, I had no chance to do anything wrong or something illegal. I enjoyed my life at full speed. I got up in the afternoon, I fell asleep at night. In the meantime, I just watched TV.

I had days when I slept for sixteen hours in a row, and for eight more hours I sat down and watched TV. I had nothing else to do. I had no work. I had sandwiches in the refrigerator. I didn't need anything else to get by. My mom took care ofeverything else.

In my fifteen years of existence, I never even made a meal myself.

I never bought food in the store. I never cared about what and how much money it costs because we could not afford it anyway.

I did not have to ask. My parents' nightly quarrels I listened to on a regular basis were mainly because of money.

They blamed the government together with Barack Obama...

They blamed their employers...

Every night, the same fights about the same topics...

Everyday I did the same thing. I spent the whole day inside the apartment like a fish in an aquarium. I didn't need to look at myself in the mirror. I experienced it, I knew that I was living a boring life. Only when I switched on the television did my life have any meaning. That little black box was one of the most amazing things in my life.

Some days I wanted to be like Michael Scofield in Prison Break. To be a smart guy with a perfectly tattooed body.

Some days I wanted to be like Brian O'Connor in Fast and Furious. Driving incredibly fast cars.

Some days I wanted to do magic tricks like Harry Potter and some days I wanted to kill people like Jason Bourne did.

In any event, I never wanted to be Tom Seed.

The movies gave me a reason to be happy, even though I faced my bullies back at school, even though our flat smelled like the black mold spreading across the walls, even though I had no friends.

Movie stars replaced everything that I did not have – friends, love, excitement...

I remember St. Patrick's Day. My parents stayed at home. Everyone had the day off. Me, my mom, my father, we sat on the old couch and watched the news on the TV. I had to partake in the TV channels that old people usually watched. From the microwave wafted the great smell of pizza, frozen pizza. One of the few foods we could afford. Bored from the long commercials, we sat down behind the table and started to chow down on our pizza. We enjoyed it, the delicious taste of the thin dough. Suddenly something interrupted our moment of joy. I heard a noise, so I went to turn off the TV. I heard a knock on the door. Someone was knocking on our door. We had no idea who it might be. Mom was sitting closer to the door, so she went to open it.

A tall man in a FedEx uniform stood outside the door. *Mrs. Seed?* He asked.

I knew it must be something important. Very important because no couriers go to the Bronx. They're too scared. The guy looked frightened too. Mom signed something, then he went away. He brought a large brown envelope. Each of us had our own idea of what might be inside. Maybe new checks? Perhaps we won something? Maybe they invited us to the Oprah Show?

I opened the envelope with my excitement building. Papers dropped from inside the envelope. A ton of documents from an insurance company based in Manhattan. The nightmare had returned to our lives. These papers stated the value of the damage caused by my stupid actions.

We had to pay $40,000 within thirty days. That lawyer had not lied to us. The insurance company had paid the costs of repairing the damaged cars, but we had to pay that amount to the insurance company. When I read it, I ran to the bathroom and threw up the pizza I had eaten a few minutes ago. I was so nervous. My whole body was shaking. I had a huge pulsing pain in my stomach.

While my mother was crying, my father started to hit me many times with a leather belt. After so many days of sitting in front of the TV, in peace, I couldn't stop myself. I couldn't bear the pain anymore.

I attacked my father.

I tried to stop him …

I failed …

My attempt did not work. Everything just got worse.

He tossed his belt and began to beat me with his hands straight on my face. I'm sure that if he had not broken my nose, which started to bleed so hard that the blood covered his whole body, he would have killed me then and there. The broken nose saved my life. After a few hard moments, my mom called an ambulance for me, and it came very quickly. They took care of me and my nose. Luckily, I did not have to go to the hospital. Of course they asked who did this to me. I told them that I slipped on the wet floor and hit my face on the table.

Yes, I was lying! But if I told them the truth, the next time a funeral car would come to our apartment, not an ambulance.

When the EMTs left, my mom asked me for the business card for that lawyer from Manhattan. She called him and tried to explain our situation, that we did not have enough money for the insurance company. It did not take long before the call ended. My mother told us with a sad voice that there was no other option, that we had to pay, otherwise we would go to court.

My parents thought it was a miracle if we would be left with some money for food at the end of the month. Less than a hundred dollars in the bank account, in our wallets just a few dollars … This was all the money we had. We did not have any jewelry, antiques, or other valuable items that we could sell. We did not even have health insurance. The most valuable thing my family owned was that old apartment, inherited from my grandparents.

We had less than thirty days to get $40,000. I knew my family was having a difficult time. My parents worked regular jobs: my mom cleaned at he fast-food chain, my father looked after the parking lot at a mall.

I never heard them complain about their work. Only about their employers. I think they liked their work, but there was one problem. Their jobs provided them with only the minimum wage, even though they worked full days. My parents did not have any friends, siblings, or other relatives to help us. As a poor family, we did not have any other option.

The next day, we all visited the bank. My mom explained our situation to the clerk sitting behind the desk. He assured us that the bank was helping people like us solve their problems. We needed to borrow $40,000. The clerk asked about our income, our expenses. Everything was entered into his computer. Then he went to the office nearby. We were sitting nervously in the huge seats while we tried to distract ourselves by admiring the decorations hanging on the wall.

Five minutes later, he came back and shared the words: *As a low-incomefamily, our bank cannot lend such a high amount. We can lend you up to $15,000. No more.*

My mother was overwhelmed with emotions. She went to her knees and asked the clerk while crying her eyes out for an exception: *Sir, $15,000 is a huge sum of money, but I need the whole amount,$40,000. We need it for an insurance company in Manhattan, not for us. Please, you are our only chance.*

The clerk returned to the same office. This time he came back with some papers and told us that the bank would lend us the whole sum, $40,000, provided we would guarantee it with our flat in the Bronx.

We agreed without hesitation. We left for home very satisfied. The bank had lent us the money, which we immediately sent to the Manhattan Insurance Company. On the same day, we had two phone calls. The first call from the Manhattan Insurance Company confirming the damage had been paid for, which meant no court for us. The second call came from that lawyer who thanked us for the serious and open discussion. Not only in words, but he also sent us a gift basket full of fruits.

My parents understood their income would not be enough to pay the monthly repayments for the loan. Solving this situation meant working harder and longer than ever before.Our flat was on the line. Everything we had.

My mother found a second job – she worked as a dog caretaker during the day, working her job at the fast food chain during the night.

My dad had to do the same thing. Throughout the day he worked as a parking guard in the shopping center, working at nights as a street sweeper.

I felt horrible. I destroyed the lives of my parents, the most important people in my life. Since I was kid, everything I did was bad. I never did anything to earn their praise me. I never did anything that would make them happy. Other children gave their parents reasons to be proud of them. I only gave my parents reasons to be disappointed in me. Everything that could go wrong, I messed up. They probably considered me to be their biggest mistake, not their greatest gift.

How could I change this situation? …

How could I help them? …

Questions that I did not know the answer to.

That horrible feeling to see them returning home late at night home, tired from their hard work, was self-evident.

They looked terrible.

Their faces had more wrinkles than ever before.

Their eyes were sadder than ever before.

After a month of hard work every day in two different jobs, my parents received their paychecks.

A well-deserved payout.

Unfortunately, after paying the bills for electricity, water, taxes, and loans, we were in the same situation as we were before with just one job.

Miserable.

It had been weeks since we had eaten together at the table as a real family.

I was tired of seeing the same episode Two and a Half Men for the second time, so I decided to get outside for some fresh air. For a long time, I roamed across the dangerous streets of the Bronx. A typical couch potato like myself, I was always faced with bullying. It was no different in the streets. Calling me various names, insults from guys driving their cars by with loud music blasting, these things didn't scare me. Barking dogs behind the fences did not scare me.

Those big guys with the knives in their hands frightened me. Because of them, I felt the ice cold touch of a knife blade on my own neck. For the first time in my life, I had the desire to be different. I no longer wanted to be the poor, weak boy who was the victim of the strong. On the streets, people were always attacking me. Guys, women, children, nobody respected me. I wanted to be that guy, with respect, with big muscles, with honor.

I saw an ad on the TV with a guy with big muscles. His name was Greg Plitt. I wanted to look like him. I wanted to be like him. Every day I started practicing with my own weight. Pushups, sit-ups, squats. I practiced up to the last drop of power in my body. Every repetition made me stronger. Every exercise I did made me more persistent. In a relatively short time I saw the results. I knew that if I want to have big muscles, I have to practice just like Greg Plitt does. In our neighborhood there was only one facility with computers available to the public for free. The public library.

I was hoping to find there what I needed to find. When I came in, I asked an older guy behind the counter where I could find information about a guy from TV. He recommended that I search the internet. I was embarrassed to tell him that I did not know how to use the internet.

No worries about it, my boy, he said.

Then he showed me the small white box with buttons called a computer. He showed me where and how to write that person's name. I sat down on the chair and typed his name – Greg Plitt, I clicked on the search button. In just a second, I found out so many exciting things about the guy.

I was overwhelmed. He served in the army before he became a fitness star. I read an interview with him where he mentioned his workout routine. I finally learned how to train. In addition to the workout routine, I also found his videos. After watching the first video,

I wanted to see more and more. I was so motivated. So, so motivated. Greg Plitt gave me the reason to keep going despite my tough life. Before I returned home, I printed out some of his photos which I stuck to the wall of my little room. I admired them for the rest of that day.

I couldn't sleep that night. I was still thinking about exercise. I imagined myself walking along the streets of the Bronx with big muscles, all the people saying hello, respecting me. I was dreaming that all those big guys were scared to look into my eyes... I couldn't get it out of my head.

The boys with the big muscles exercise at the gym with iron, not at home in front of the TV. My inner voice was whispering: soon I had to start high school, and I had to be in good shape. Otherwise, I would be a victim of bullies again like in kindergarten and elementary school. I createdsuch abig issue formy parents already, I couldn't burden them with anything else. I had to find a reasonable solution for how to train in a real gym with real equipment.

After a sleepless night, the idea hit me. My neighbor had muscles like Greg. I figured he had to train with iron. Without hesitation I got up from my bed and went out into the corridor directly in front of his door. There was loud music coming out of his apartment. I think I heard Eminem. I knocked on his door. I had to knock more times because of that loud music. After a moment, the door opened and my strong neighbor stood in front of me. I asked him where he trains. He kindly told me that there is a small gym in our block of flats, in the cellar, and if I was interested I could train with him there.

Of course I agreed with that idea. I couldn't believe it. A fitness center in the basement of our block of flats!

The next morning I was excitedly waiting in front of the locked door to the cellar gym. I had no idea when my neighbor Gary was going to practice, so I sat there on the stairs and waited. I sat there for a few hours until I heard a few voices. Some guys were walking down the stairs. Three guys big as NFL players: my neighbor Gary and his two buddies – Ray and Patrick. Each of them had the same haircut, short hair and muscles showing strong veins. Their bodies looked like a map with an engraved path. If I met one of them on the street, I would not have the courage to stand up to him.

When I stood in front of them on the stairs, in front of the cellar gym, I felt blessed that I was given the chance to spend time with them.

My neighbor, Gary, put his massive arm on my shoulder, looked straight into my eyes and said: *Three years ago I sold drugs on the streets. I was the best dealer. I had a lot of money, more than I needed. Instead of spending, I saved everything. One night I was caught by the cops, and they arrested me. I spent two years in prison. There I found my passion. Passion in exercise. After I was released, I bought the equipment from my savings and opened up this gym. In the past, I used to give people crap on the street that destroyed their lives and the lives of their families. Now I give the same people a place where they can develop, work on themselves.*

At that moment, I realized I had been wrong. Not all people in the Bronx are evil.

After entering the gym, I entered paradise. My dreams had come true. Machines, dumbbells, weights, kettlebells, boxing bags. The walls were covered with posters of Arnold Schwarzenegger, Ronnie Coleman, Muhammad Ali, The Rock. A real Paradise. My eyes were shining like the eyes of a small child in Disneyland.

Gary asked me why I decided to train. I told him the truth. The cruel truth about how the other guys were bullying me, how I was held up with a knife, how Greg Plitt motivated me.

You cannot run away from fear all the time, you have to stand up to it, overcome it, he assured me.

I did not have any experience with exercising in the gym on the machines or with dumbbells, so I needed a bit of help. Ray willingly showed me the correct technique for many exercises, while Patrick was training on the bench press and Gary was observing him. My muscles were on fire. They literally burned. It hurt, but I loved the pain. This pain was different. It made me stronger. After an hour of heavy exercise I stood in front of the mirror, closed my eyes and imagined how I would look with a perfect body. The idea was motivational for me, making me happy.

That place made me happy. These guys made me happy. Even though I looked like a skeleton, I did not worry me. That was the reason why I came there. To change it.

By the way, I heard something from those guys that I hadn't heard from anyone before. Words of praise, encouragement, thanks and support. When I came home, I opened the refrigerator and picked out two sandwiches, which I immediately ate. Usually I turned on the TV at that time to watch the Simpsons, Breaking Bad, or NCIS:Los Angeles, but this exercise made me so tired that I laid in bed and immediately fell asleep. No need or mood to watch those yellow Simpsons or some crime series.

The gym had become my second home. I spent more time there than at home. There I learned to be responsible, disciplined, patient. I did things I was never allowed to do at home.

Painted the walls.

Vacuumed the carpets.

Cleaned the toilets.

All members paid a monthly membership fee, except for me. I was not only the gym member. I was the one in charge of that gym.

I considered Gary to be more than just my boss. I started to see him as my best friend.

Since my very first day at high school, I was a trouble-maker. I faced many issues. Different issues than the ones I encountered in elementary school or primary school. I had to be at two different places at the same moment. In school and in the gym. During lessons, I listened to boring lectures from boring teachers, and during breaks I ran over to the gym to unlock and lock the door again for fans of big muscles. This experience taught me the feeling of having to care for so many things at the same time, just like my parents did. Surprisingly it worked. My teachers did not complain. Neither did my gym mates. Nobody complained. It was only my issue. I flew from one place to the other like a bird. I did not enjoy it at all. To be quite honest, I hated it.

As expected, my muscles gave me the respect that I believed I deserved. Also, changing my hairstyle helped me too. I no longer wore my hair longer like I did before. Every day, I shaved my head with my father's razor in our bathroom. I looked like a tough guy, not a momma's boy. In class, I became one of the most respected people. The other guys showed me respect. They said hi to me, shook my hands, asked me how I was doing. Completely different behavior than in the past.

Time at school passed incredibly slowly. I had to learn things that I had no interest in knowing. I had to sit cluelessly and wait for the deafening ringing of the bell, which always caused a traffic jam at the school exit. At school I only enjoyed the breaks. Long breaks. Only then I could leave the torturous classrooms for my beloved gym. I did not see any sense in being a student. My teachers still talked and talked in the hopes that someone was listening to them, but no one listened to them. Nobody!

Once I told my teacher that the television taught me more than he taught me. He did not argue with me.

After six months of attending high school, I decided to quit. No one could stop me. My mom and my father worked for days at their jobs. Home for them was just a couple of hours in bed. They had no chance to find out. And even if they find out, I wouldn't care.

I preferred the gym to the school.

A place where I could spend the whole day with a smile on my face.

A place that gave me more than school ever gave me.

A place that completed me.

A place I got real friends.

A place I got real results. Visible results.

I had a better relationship with those guys than I had with my own parents. They supported me, and I supported them. They took care of me, and I took care of them. They were my real family. I could walk down the streets because the enemies of my past had become the brothers of my present. Everyone in the Bronx knew who Tom Seed was. Everyone knew me.

This never would have happened if I had not started practicing at Gary's basement gym.

Exercise gave me a self-confidence that I never had. Exercise gave me self-esteem that I never had. Exercise gave me the respect that I never had. Exercise gave me the friends I never had.

It all started with one knife under my neck. It all began with one fitness star on a TV advertisement.

I had so much to do that I completely forgave my parents for our family issues. To be honest, I also forgot about my parents. My mom, my dad. I didn't miss them at all.

I didn't hear from them all day. I never even saw them during the day. You know, I felt deep in my heart that I loved them. They gave me a place to live. They gave me food. Solved all my problems!

Without them, I could not have solved anything. I'm grateful for that.

But they gave me only the basic things necessary for survival...

They satisfied my external needs while my heart was injured. No feelings of love. No feelings of importance. No feelings of home. Even though I did a lot of bad things, I deserved the love of my parents.

One October morning I got up early, as usual. With Gary, I agreed to wash the gym from floor to ceiling. As usual, I put on my heavy black tracksuit with the same white t-shirt I wore every day. I was about to brush my teeth when I heard something strange. Strange sounds coming out of my parents' room. I have to confess, I was a little scared. I did not know what it might be. I was wearing a t-shirt with a v-neck, so I was hoping that if the thief saw my big muscles, he would get scared and run away. I took a few uncertain steps, and then I opened the door to my parents' bedroom.

I didn't find any thief there. I didn't find any animals. My mother lay in bed, so small and tiny. My mom who I hadn't seen for months. I asked her what was happening. She looked like a mummy, completely white. Without energy, she told me she did not feel well, she was probably sick. I touched her forehead, it was burning hot.

She was sweaty all over. The high temperature had immediately overtaken her. I didn't know what to do, so I just stood there hopelessly, staring at her as she suffered.

All of the sudden, I remembered what to do in such a situation. I saw it in the movies. I took a cloth from the kitchen, soaked it in cold water and laid it on her hot face. It helped her. Besides, I brought her a glass of water and I told her to get some more sleep.

I couldn't stay any longer with her. I had to go. In the gym I was sweeping all the carpets, washing the floors, cleaning the mirrors and toilets. Finally, I disinfected the dumbbells and machines.

I had finished cleaning, and the gym was bright and shiny. Back in the apartment I checked up my sick mother. In such a short time, her health had gotten much worse. A cough, high fever. I did not need to be Doctor House to find out what disease she had. She had the flu. The common flu, she only needed to lie in the warm bed to get rid of it. I made her some warm tea from sliced onion. I couldn't do anything more for her. After a busy morning, I was finally able to pay attention just to myself and my friends. Of course in the gym.

Gary brought a new edition of the magazine Muscle & Fitness, the Bible for every fitness lover. At school, I had to read books, learn about the past, do my homework. I hated it. But to read these fitness magazines, I had a completely different relationship with reading. I loved it. I read articles about bodybuilders, their advice, their regular workouts, their eating habits and their enthusiasm.

On that day, I returned home late in the evening. Of course, I wasn't in a good mood. My mom had created this bad mood for. I didn't feel comfortable. I always had the whole apartment just to myself, I only lived there by myself. Since my mother's illness, she spent her time at home, not at work as usual. I was used to be home alone without my parents. My daily ritual was disrupted. I just hoped that my mom would recover as soon as possible so that she would be able to get back to work again. She'll be at work, I'll be alone at home. In peace and quiet.

The phone rang the next morning. I picked it up. Mom's boss from the fast food joint called. He asked me in a very angry voice where my mother was, screaming at the top of his lungs why she wasn't coming to work. I told him that my mother was sick and that she would not return for the next few days. Without saying anything, he ended the call. I assumed it was not important, so I didn't tell my mother about it.

Twenty minutes later, the phone rang again.

The same guy in his croaking voice told me the following: *I'm sorry, boy, your mother is no longer working for me …* I was speechless. How could he do something like that? My mom had been working there every day for years, and he sacked her just because she was lying at home in bed sick with a high fever. I couldn't' keep this "pleasant" message to myself.

I just went to my mom and sadly told her about the phone call from her boss. Her former boss.

She accepted it with grace. She just told me: *alright, Tom.*

Nothing else. She did not complain, she did not scream, she did not cry. I expected a completely different attitude. Due to her health condition, she did not have the strength to walk or for work. Standing on her feet was an issue for her. The common flu, normally cured in a few days, had plagued my mom for more than a month. Just skin and bones, she was lying in bed all day. On her body, red spots appeared due to her long-term condition. An irritating dry cough prevented her from sleeping. Still coughing, all day and all night, and it was still getting worse. I'm afraid that even the black mold on the walls of our apartment hurt her more. As a poor family we could not afford medicine or a doctor. We did not have health insurance. For others, of course this was a normal thing, but for us it was only a dream.

I spent most of my time at home. I did not have time to practice. I did not have time for anything. While my father worked, I was taking care of my sick mother. I was very bothered to see my mother in such a condition. I wanted to help her, but I could not. Our family again faced a difficult time. Again and again.

We received a kind reminder from the bank that we hadn't paid the loan. Then we received another reminder from the power plant. We hadn't paid the electricity bills. The financial situation in our family looked critical. It had never been this bad. Even though my father had two different jobs, we did not have enough money. We kept receiving new and new bills – for electricity, water, television. Dad's salary paid only a fraction of these bills. We had no money left over. My father had to borrow some money for food from his colleagues at work. Otherwise, we would be starving. After these events, my mom became a shell of her former self. She hurt herself dramatically, she did not talk to us, she did not eat anything. She closed herself. Also, dad's relationship with us changed. He blamed me and my mother for the situation we were in.

He was right. I did it. I've done everything wrong. I was responsible for this.

Unpaid bills brought fear, extra burdens, and tension to our lives, but the red envelope that came brought disaster to our family.

When we took a loan from the bank, we guaranteed our only property – the flat we lived in. At that time, we had no idea what this would mean to us. We were given two days to leave the apartment. Then the bank would take it. We immediately called the bank. We visited the bank in person. We asked a lawyer from Manhattan for help. No positive results. They had no interest in helping us. They only cared about our apartment. Nothing else. I felt so helpless. I could not sleep. I could not calm myself down. I was still thinking about what would happen to me, my family if …

For certain reasons, we did not tell my mother about this situation, because if she knew, it would have disastrous consequences for her. On the first day, we stayed in our apartment with the hope that they maybe they would consider leaving us there. We were wrong.

The next morning, a guy came very early in a gray suit with two cops. The cops urged us to leave the apartment without any grief. I tried hard to explain to them what would happen to us when we lost the apartment. We did not have any other option. Either we leave the apartment voluntarily, or we will be kicked out with our hands tied.

I took just three sandwiches out of the refrigerator into my bag. Nothing else. With tears in my eyes I entered my parents' room and explained to my mother why the cops were in the apartment. I do not think she heard me at all. I lifted her out of bed and put her in my arms. Away from our apartment. I wanted to fight them, to stand up to them, to protect our apartment. But if I did it, I would go to jail, and my mom and my dad would be all alone. I was only sixteen years old.

Cold November weather. Frost and snow. An excellent time of year – for people in their warm homes, and a devastating time for homeless people. We did not have any place to warm up. We did not have anywhere to sleep. We did not have any place to go. The old apartment, inherited from my grandparents, was confiscated by the bank. Besides that, we did not have anything. I wanted to go downstairs to Gary's gym in the basement to ask him for help. Gary would help us, but without a blink of an eye, we had to leave not only the apartment but also the whole building.

With my sick mother in my arms I walked through the cold streets of the Bronx. Even though she weighed less than eighty pounds, my legs were weak all the way.

The hardest steps of my life.

Unbearable pain in my muscles, in my bones. It tortured me.

We went to my dad's work two miles away. Completely frozen, we came to the shopping mall.

My father sat there in a small booth from which he guarded the parking lot. When he saw us, he knew what had happened. The expression on his face revealed it.

He told us he was going to go to the dressing room. He came back ten minutes to pick us up. We were supposed to wait for him, so we were waiting for him as he told us. Even though it was snowing and our clothes and our shoes were completely soaked, we stayed there until it got dark.

Then I realized that my father would not come back to us again.

He left us. He just left us forever.

He let us out in the winter like animals.

If we stayed out there, we would not have survived until morning. We had to find a warm place to stay. To warm up, to dry. With my last amounts of energy I walked through the dark streets looking for a place to stay. Any place to sleep in. The motel was not an option. Already out of the money we had with us, we could not even buy a decent meal. We found a place to stay only in our Bronx. An old abandoned garage provided us shelter from the wet snow. We went to a corner where we tried to survive that night. We could not sleep. It was so cold. Our bodies were shaking like crazy. We were literally frozen alive.

That's the day I lost my home, my father, my friends.

After a few hours of struggling with the cold, I fell asleep. I did not know how I did it, but when I woke up, I felt like someone was killing me alive. My entire body was really in pain. All my fingers were burning. I had survived that night. Fortunately, my sick mother also survived. But the fever remained. It was so cold and she was burning. The day before, I lost a lot of things except one. I knew if we stayed in the Bronx, some of my friends would soon see me homeless. I could not do that. I would lose my pride. The only thing left for me.

I did not mean to be ashamed. With just five dollars in the wallet, we headed to Manhattan. We had to stop very often, to rest and let me catch my breath. After a challenging journey, we arrived in Manhattan. The place where all our problems started. I believed that the local rich people would help us. They would feel regret after seeing us.

I knocked on all the doors in that neighborhood. Not one opened. Disappointed from the lack of interested, we sat on an empty street next to some large black containers that formed a barrier for us with the outside world. In one container I found an old brown torn blanket that I used to cover my mom with. Besides the blanket, I found nothing useful.

The condition of my ill mom had deteriorated rapidly. She needed help. I left her alone on the street, hidden behind the containers, while I went to the streets. To beg.

I felt uncomfortable, embarrassed, humiliated. While I was asking people, unknown people for money, my conscience did not allow me to look into their eyes. I lost my pride, but I had no choice. Some people took a picture of me. Some people laughed at me and some people threatened me. I imagined myself jumping from a skyscraper and my suffering would be over.

The only reason I did not do it was my mom, she needed me. She gave me the only reason not to end it all. Stopping and reaching out to people passing by did not work. So I sat down on the edge of the sidewalk in the hope that I could beg for at least a few bucks. At the end of the day I was so done with it all. It was not worth it. I got less than two dollars for one day. It was hardly enough to buy a grilled onion cheddar burger at McDonald's.

The days on the street were hard and the nights even harder. We suffered from the cold. Hunger and thirst forcing me to get up and beg again. The people who gave me a few dollars for the previous day in sorrow disappeared. I only faced insults, abuse, humiliation. Their hard words hurt me. I sat at the edge of the sidewalk like a total loser. Even the dogs did not stop for me.

A group of young guys noticed this and took advantage of it. They provoked me. They were throwing cigarettes at me. They spit on me. They even recorded it. They laughed at me while I was raving. They treated me like a total waste! No respect, no respect at all.

I stood up, grabbed one of those guys by his sweatshirt and hit him with my right hand right in his face. They got scared. They ran away from me. To be sure, I did the same.

I had only passed a few streets when I found myself in front of the same group of young guys. This time, their group had many more members than before. Almost all of them dressed in oversized clothes. They looked like rappers from elementary school.

They did not want to talk to me about my life or about my hobbies. They wanted to fight with me. To get some revenge.

I had no chance of fighting them. I stood there alone. I started running away from them like a little boy before a storm. I ran until I found some safety.

I had lost my self-confidence that I had gained from exercising so hard in the gym.

I had lost my courage, gained in the gym.

I had lost my strength, gained in thegym.

I had lost my respect, gained in the gym.

I hated myself.

The longer I lived on the street, the more I felt anger towards my surroundings, I hated the things around me. Guys at my age were going to school in new cars, dates with blue-eyed blondes, playing basketball. And me?

I lived on the streets with my sick mother, like two useless pieces of trash.

My mother started coughing up blood. There was nothing else left, just to take her to the doctor. I went to the office without even knocking on the door, and I showed my mom to the doctor. I asked him for help. He did not feel comfortable telling me that my mom had a huge problem with her lungs. Immediately she had to be taken to the hospital. He warned me that treating this disease without health insurance costs nine hundred dollars. I explained to him that we had no money for food, and especially not for such an expensive treatment. He excused himself and hadus let out of his office by a security guard.

How can you be so selfish? How can you be so cruel? No interest in helping my mom! I cried…

Despair, hopelessness, disappointment, hatred. All these feelings were at the forefront of my mind. In this world, people only cared about money, nothing else. We did not matter to them, us poor people. People walking down the street looked at me as I held my mother in my arms with misunderstanding, I saw it in their eyes. Trying to avoid us instead of trying to help us.

For more than three weeks we had been sleeping on the streets as real homeless people. For a few days, we hadn't eaten food like human beings. All the shelters were full. All the warm, dry places that had access for people like us, forbidden. The hunger and cold were unbearable. My clothes looked like the clothes of a scarecrow.

My muscles had disappeared.

I looked like a skeleton, just skin and bone.

Near our "camp," they opened up a small grocery store. Only one older worker was there. I took the opportunity to feed us. With a hood on my head, I hid bread, hot dogs, and dried meat under my sweatshirt, and without being noticed I left the shop. The worker didn't have the time to notice it. He was too busy. I knew that theft is a crime, but I did it for survival. Not for pleasure. After a long time, we finally had enough food for the next few days.

Back when we were home in our apartment, I used to eat my food so quickly. I took it as a sure thing of course. But I ate it very slowly on the street, enjoying every bite. I didn't leave one crumb to the rats hanging around us.

Food helped me to calm down my hunger, but not for my mom. She needed something more important – medication. People living on the streets die from winter and sickness. I could not allow my mom to die the same way. For the first time in my life, I stole food from the store and I succeeded. I thought I could do it a second time. With medicine.

Near us, I found three pharmacies. In the first pharmacy, many people were shopping all the time, it would be too risky. So I just asked what medicine is best for the lungs. The pharmacist recommended a Swiss medicine costing thirty-eight dollars to me.

In the second pharmacy, I couldn't do anything. They had already closed.

My last and only chance was the third pharmacy on Canal Street. Through the window, I saw that there was no one except a saleswoman. I entered the shop, greeting her politely. Confidently I asked for the Swiss medicine for thirty-eight dollars, which the first pharmacy had recommended. She put it on the counter and asked if I could afford to buy it.

Of course, no problem, I told her.

She packed it into my bag, handed it to me and asked for $38. I pretended to pull the money out of my back pocket of my jeans. Then I ran away. With the medicine in the bag. Of course without paying.

I was so excited and so scared.

I said to myself: yes, yes, I did it.

My mother will finally be healthy like she used to be.

I was running through busy streets crowded with people, among whom I looked like a loser, while inside of me I felt like a winner.

In a short time I had stolen from two different shops without being noticed. Nobody caught me. No one punished me. I thought I was untouchable. To celebrate my victory, I stopped at a big shopping mall. For a moment I preferred my pleasure and not my mother's health. I knew that nothing would happen to her when I came back with the medicine later. I was caring for her all the time, right?

I just wanted to have time for myself.

The mall looked huge. Glass windows, dozens of shops, Christmas decorations, happy people with full shopping bags, restaurants with mouthwatering food. Such an amazing sight. I went to the store that attracted me the most. The bakery. Every piece of their cakes looked like artwork. Red. White. Blue. So many different varieties. I could not resist them.

I took three chocolate desserts and I quickly ran away from there. Again no one caught me. In a good mood, I sat down on a bench close to the escalator where I enjoyed the delicious taste of chocolate. I tell you, it was the most delicious sweet taste I ever ate.

The moment I decided stand up and get back to my mom, somebody grabbed my hand. I looked up, frightened.

I was looking straight into the eyes of a guy in uniform. A guy from security. He took me into a small, dirty room with flat screens on the walls. There he showed me the video footage from the camera, as I was stealing those desserts.

Obviously, I was not untouchable.

I was stupid.

The security guy looked through my sweatshirt and found nothing in it. Then he searched my medicine bag. It seemed suspicious that I was missing a receipt. He saw the name of the pharmacy on the bag, so he called to check it out. He probably called the young saleswoman who told him I had stolen the drugs, because he called the police as his second call. When he called, he locked the door and left me there alone only with my fear. He came back to me with two cops. He showed them the same video as he did to me.

Without any unnecessary questions, they took me to the police station. I knew what was waiting for me.

I had broken the conditions set by the court. My hands were shaking, my head was shaking. I felt horrible.

In less than two hours, they accused me of two thefts and I was to be immediately sent to the juvenile correction center.

I had reconciled myself with the punishment set by the court, but I could not live with the fact that I was leaving my mom alone out there. I went to the judge asking for help for my mother, which she needed. He allowed me to go see her. Thanks to the judge, I could help my mother before I began serving a sentence of one year in the correctional facility.

With my hands tied, I got into the white van, among the other young criminals.

Even though we lived different lives, even though we came from different families, even though we grew up in different environments, even though we had a different skin color, we all had one thing in common: we had broken the law.

The police officer in charge of the truck stopped close to the street I knew all too well. He opened the door and escorted me to my mother. From a distance, I saw her lying on the ground beside the container. I tried to wake her up.

I screamed at her. I shook her. She did not respond. She was lying there unconscious. The police officer pushed me off and began to revive her.

In the meantime, he called through the ambulance's radio. Then he took me back to the van. I sat there afraid for my mother's life.

While the doctors did everything to save her life, I had done nothing. Nothing!

Our van was about to leave, and I had to get used to the feeling that I would not see my mom for the next twelve months. During a long journey by van, I looked out through the frozen window to the outside world. The world I was leaving. After arriving at the correction center, we were all sorted into one line. We stood there in the hopes that this was all just a bad dream. But it was not a dream. It was reality. A harsh reality. We had to get undressed, take a shower and get dressed in new clothes. I received a small cozy room with just a bed and toilet. The security doors closed, then the lights went out.

There was a silence in the whole facility, while my mind was in such chaos. I could not sleep. I was only thinking about my mom.

Was she alive?

Had she died?

What if she needed me?

What if she's looking for me?

I felt this incredibly horrible feeling all over my body.

I felt terrible for the first few weeks in that facility.

Very bad.

I could not sleep.

I could not eat.

I could not concentrate.

I wasted all my time lost in my own thoughts, feeling guilty.

My own thoughts were killing me alive.

My body was locked in that small room, but my mind was somewhere else.

In other words, nowhere.

Just when I was about to collapse, a ray of hope came into my life. The director of the facility invited me to his dark, wood-covered office. I expected some good news about my mother. Instead, he told me with regret that my mother had died.

I did not say a word. I did not let out any tears. I just sat there in the chair and looked out into empty space.

Only during the night was I able to give into my feelings and emotions. I cried.

I cried because I realized what I had done. I killed my mom. Because of me, my parents took out the loan. Because of me, my parents lost our home. Because of me, my father left us. Because of me, we slept in the street. Because of me, my mom died. I felt a terrible hatred of myself.

My mother stood by me when I opened my eyes for the first time. I did not stand by her when she closed her eyes the last time.

I did not want to live any longer. I did not want to breathe anymore. Staying in this correction facility was not my punishment. My punishment was to live with the guilt of what my actions had done to my family, to the people around me and to me.

From that day, I fell into depression. A deep depression.

I spent most of my time thinking about death.

Only one thought made me happy. I imagined at least a thousand times that people, crying people, were standing above my coffin, remembering me as a good person with his heart in the right place. A character with tremendous and praise worthy actions. I was not afraid of death. I was afraid of my future. I was scared of what was out there waiting for me.

The new director at the facility came up with some new rules. One of those rules affected me a lot. I had to work. In my case, this meant washing the floor for the whole facility. I was given basic instructions on how to wash and where

I had to put the dirty water. After a short training, I picked up a metal bucket and mop and went to work.

Every sound I heard scared me.

Every guy I met scared me.

Everything scared me then.

I had no self-confidence. I washed the first floor relatively quickly. On the second floor, my strength came back. There was an unbearable pain in my back. Every movement made me mad. I had blood streaks on my palms, tears in my eyes. I could not continue washing.

I sat down on the floor and breathed heavily.

Inhale. Exhale. Inhale. Exhale. It did not take long before someone noticed I had stopped washing. I showed them my bloody palms, but they did not care at all. They insisted that my task to be done. With extreme effort I stood up on my own feet, dipped the mop into the water and continued what I had to do. Wash the floors.

I concentrated more on my pain than on the cleanliness of the floor. I concentrated more often on my pain than what I was actually doing. That was the only way for job to get done. When I got into the room with the other convicts, all of them looked at me with unpleasant expressions. I clenched my teeth and washed the faster than I ever knew,even through the cruel pain, just to avoid having to face "those kind" people.

Tired, bloody tired as a packhorse, I finally finished all the floors. A common, household mop forced me to reach to the limits of my own strength.

I first thought that washing the floors was a stupid activity. I did it just because I had to do it.

But later I began to think it was the best thing that happened to me in that facility. Thanks to this job, I was so busy that I did not have time to think of death, which helped me overcome my depression.

My appetite returned.

My desire to live returned.

Hard work fulfilled me. I was getting into shape.

I felt like I was back in Gary's basement gym.

Of course, it had its dark side too.

The third floor.

The place I came back from with blue bruises on my body. The criminals from that floor waited for me to first finish the job before they started with me.

They beat me without any sorrow.

This situation was repeated every day.

First and second floor paradise, third floor hell.

Twelve months later.

After those very difficult twelve months, they released me.

I had come there with something, but I left with nothing. Only one person talked to me. The director of the facility. He shook my hand, wished me happiness in my life, and we all went our own way. He into his office, me into my white van.

As a minor, without my parents I had to live in a local shelter for people in need.

I had no big expectations. When I arrived there, in the old and dirty part of New York, an old blue-haired woman was waiting for me. She was dressed in a black dress. She welcomed me with a fake smile. Then she took me inside. She showed me the rooms of a modest shelter. One small kitchen with a round wooden table, a bathroom, a room with tools and bedrooms with beds. I got a room with another six people. From that lady I realized that all the people living there don't pay anything for accommodation. They work it out.

I barely had the chance to lie down on my new bed before that blue-haired grandmother called me into the corridor. From there she brought me into the bright room with the tools. To their workshop. Hinges, hammers and other tools hung on the walls. Everything you could have ever imagined. I had never seen many of them before. I did not know what their purpose was. Then she showed me what to do and how to do it. Take one piece, apply the glue, take the second part and join them together. Take one piece, use the glue, take the second part and join them together.

Over and over again.

I had to make stupid brooms ...

The old wounds had not healed yet, and more were added. Apparently, the old lady was not very happy with my work, as I did not hear anything besides her criticism. She could always find something she did not like. When she criticized me or insulted me, I just kept held tongue. I did not fight back. I did not change her mind. I did not dare to do it. I have always tried to do what others asked me to do, like a broom that everybody uses to clean the floors with.

I do not know how many brooms I made, I suppose it had to be hundreds. With my sticky fingers, I turned off the light in the workshop and left for the kitchen. There I got soap that could get rid of the dried glue on my aching fingers. On the table, I had a piece of bread with strawberry jam. I knew very well what to do with it. I literally wolfed it down. After the exhausting journey from the correction facility, I was able to eat something.

My stomach made strange sounds, like horror movie. Apparently, the piece of bread surprised me.

Not a day in a new environment, and the old lady was the only person I saw there. I'm out of prison. I felt relieved inside. After an exhausting amount of hard work, I lay in bed between the cockroaches that could not prevent me from falling right asleep. But I didn't sleep for long.

A nightmare woke me up. I dreamt that my mom had died in my arms. I literally leapt out of bed. I looked around. I did not see anyone there. I was lying there alone. I approached the window in the rusty frame, through which I observed the world around me.

Lights on buildings. Stars in the sky. Cars on the road. Pedestrians on the sidewalk.

Behind this window was the real world. Behind this window were all great things. I spoke to myself...

I stood there until the first rays of sunlight struck my sad face. As it used to be my habit, I made the bed like I used to do in prison, then I moved to the kitchen. Three elderly men sat behind the table. They looked like members of a gang. Colorful dragons and snakes decorated their arms. I just hoped they were nice, friendly human beings. With a weird feeling in my stomach I sat down between them at the table. For as long as I was eating the bread, they watched me. They were focused on me. They kept looking at me. I'm sure my chewing was heard by all of them. After a careful analysis of my face, and my eyes, one of them asked if I had some cigarettes. I explained politely that I was a non-smoker. Fortunately, he accepted it positively.

When they left, I felt relieved. I felt much more at ease. The old lady, who began to test my patience, soon came to the room.

How could you sit on your lazy ass and do nothing. This is not a hotel young man. If you want to live here, you have to earn it. She screamed at me.

The vein on her forehead was a visible as the golden tooth of Harry Lime in Home Alone. I was not in the mood to listen to her speech about work ethic. I got to work. At least the brooms had no mouth. They did not complain. During my work, I forgot my negative thoughts. My mind opened up. I began to think about myself, about my life, about my future.

Why should I do this hard work for free if I can do the same thing out there for real money. My parents were able to work two different jobs. Why couldn't I do that too. I was seventeen years old, and someone was still commanding me what to do. I began to think: I found myself in this shelter only because I had no relatives. I have no one to take care of me. But that does not mean I have to stay here.

I decided to find a real job outside the shelter and pay for cheap accommodation somewhere in the city. They could not hold me there against my will.

My plan was confirmed by the arrival of the five guys to my room. My roommates. I was honored to know their dark side. They arrived late at night with a great amount of noise. They had fun all night, listened to loud music, and smoked. They smoked marijuana. I knew the smell. The same smell used to spread through the streets of the Bronx. Above all, I pretended to be deeply asleep, but I was angry in my mind. I could not sleep. Their primitive talk prevented me from doing so. I did not recognize them personally, but nevertheless I knew that friendship would never be a thing for us.

I was so tired from the previous night that I exploded. I told the old lady that I am not her slave and to find someone else she can control. I recommended she look for somebody in the Central Park Zoo. From the table I took my breakfast and disappeared from that place. Out of that hole. Like a ghost. Forever.

No bars.

No locks.

No protection.

No weapons.

Nothing could stop me.

Nothing could have prevented me from leaving.

I walked through the streets with one purpose only. To find a paid job.

Again, I had no big expectations. I would take any job. I visited every shop, every restaurant, every business I saw. I was talking to owners, vendors, secretaries. Some listened to me, some ignored me. In any case, I fought. I did not give up. I continued my search.

After so many refusals, I finally succeeded. I had done it.

In an old Italian restaurant on Bedford Street they were looking for help in the kitchen. They asked for my previous experience. I confidently told them that I recently worked as a dishwasher in one facility and also as a manual worker in a local carpenter's workshop.

I didn't tell them the truth, but I wasn't lying. I just didn't tell the whole story.

I signed some papers, stripped off my gray sweatshirt and the real job could finally start.

All day I washed dirty plates. So many plates. Even though it was really boring work, my excitement did not go away. I still had a smile on my face. I felt fantastic.

During my break, my boss asked me where I was living. I told him embarrassingly that I was currently looking for a place to stay. He willingly offered me a small room above his restaurant. I accepted his offer. And just like that, my housing issues were simply resolved. We agreed that the cost for the accommodation will be deducted from my salary.

In my seventeen years of age, I had found my first job. A perfect job. I had secure accommodation and food.

I put all my energy into the job. Because I knew that the more hours I work, the more I'll earn.

I worked every day, from early morning to late at night. Seven days a week.

I bought some new clothes with my first paycheck.

Pants, t-shirts, sweatshirts, shoes…

Finally, I could walk outdoors among the people without feeling any shame, thanks to my new outfits from famous brands. Among the people, I started to feel self-confident. My status had increased. My self-esteem had increased. I think that for the first time in my life, I felt more like someone else. I was no longer outside the crowd because of my poor looks. Since I started wearing nicer clothes, people on the street just saw me as normal.

My efforts at work were regularly rewarded. Not just with money, but also with trust. I was part of something. In the kitchen, I was one of the smartest and hardest-working guys. I always got the tasks that required more responsibility. From a simple dirty dishwasher in the kitchen, I started working as a chef's assistant. I starting learning more about my colleagues. I learned new skills like cooking, baking.

At that place, I really felt loved.

Everything I did, I did it the best way I knew. And it worked. I did not need a day off or a two-week vacation. I enjoyed my work. It brought some sense of regularity to my life. It did not take long before my boss gave me even more responsibilities than before. From the mysterious kitchen straight to the battlefield, out among the guests.

I had a new task: to serve guests. I became a waiter. I was a little afraid at first. I thought I wasn't good enough for that position. My voice was shaking, I stammered, I was sweating.

Then I found out that I had no reason to be afraid. The guests behaved very kindly to me. And often they left a tip for me.

I remember one week when we were very busy at the restaurant. All my colleagues were watching the New York Giants game. In my opinion, they were wasting their time as the Giants always lost. The next day, we celebrated the birth of Timothy's daughter, our boss, who held a big celebration at his Long Island home.

While they were having fun I was working hard in the restaurant. Without any breaks. I preferred responsibility over entertainment. I was in charge of everything. Cooking, dishwashing, washing the toilets and floors. And, of course, the most important thing, the service for our guests. Demanding guests and modest guests. Nice guests and arrogant guests. Fancy guests and modestly dressed guests. Neither of them noticed any missing staff, or a change in the taste of our food. No one!

The whole restaurant was run by only one person: me. I did it perfectly. And I enjoyed it up to the last moment. My feelings about myself grew tremendously. Pride flowed through my veins. Those days I went to sleep with an incredible feeling of a job well done.

It was two days later when the rest of the team joined me and everything went back to normal. I did mind it a bit. Actually, I minded it a lot. Attention was no longer paid only to me. I was not the only one who received recognition from the guests, from the boss. There were other guys who shared the important little things with me. The times when it was just me under the spotlight were over. I just relied on the fact that Timothy, my boss, wouldn't forget who had helped his restaurant when it mattered the most.

During our lunch break, I sat down with one of the chefs behind a table where we ate fresh pineapple pizza.

I didn't even have a chance to touch it because Timothy called me to his office. I had ever seen a bigger mess, not even in the kitchen. All sorts of staples, notes, shredded papers, newspaper photos, empty boxes of food. I sat there on a chair covered with cobwebs, and in my head, I imagined how I would takeover the management of Timothy's restaurant. How I would manage it to win prizes from the Mayor's Office for the Best Restaurant of the Year. I had worked there in so many different job positions. Except for one.

My exciting ideas were interrupted by Timothy's shouts. *I trusted you! You were like my son. I wanted to make you the boss of my restaurant, but you messed it all up. You're such a disappointment!*

I had no idea what he was talking about. Did I do something wrong? I had no idea. So I asked him for an explanation.

During the weekend, when you working here, you served a group of people. Very wealthy people from Manhattan. You probably could recognize them. They wore white custom tailor-made suits. On that day, you did everything perfectly, but a few years ago you did something terrible. Something unacceptable. You destroyed some cars. People's property. And by the way, those rich men in the white suits, they used to own those cars. They knew you, Tom. They didn't forget about it. And you lied to me. I do not want to have anything to do with people like you.

He told me that. Then he placed my paycheck on the table and told me to leave his restaurant.

I felt a strong blow right to my heart. I didn't understand how he could do this to me. How could he throw me out after all this? I looked into his eyes with disappointment. I went to the kitchen where I hugged the chef. That's how shocked I was –I started crying in his embrace. He knew what had happened. Everyone around me knew what had happened. They tried to comfort me, to calm me down. Unnecessarily. The more they tried to help me, the worse I felt.

I had worked so hard there.

I had felt so good there.

I had gotten so much recognition there.

I had enjoyed so many fun memories there.

And I lost it all because of such foolishness from such a long time ago...

Jobless and homeless. I left that place with only a gym bag full of clothing. I had only eighty dollars in my wallet. I didn't save any money from my previous paydays. I spent them onthe clothes I had in that bag. If I had not received my pay that day, I would have had nothing. I could not stay without income for long. I would not have survived it. I could not do it myself. Sadness, disappointment, all that was replaced by anger. I had a desire, a strong desire to prove to Timothy that he had made the biggest mistake of his life. The best way I could get my revenge was to work for his competition. For another Italian restaurant. And I didn't need any GPS navigation to get there. I had no need for any map. I knew exactly where to go.

There were two similar Italian restaurants in the neighborhood, the owners of whom I personally met.

I went to the first restaurant and before I tried to say something, they shooed me out of the restaurant. I obviously had more experience than they required. But it didn't bother me. On the contrary, it only strengthened my desire to prove Timothy wrong.

I had to walk faster to the second restaurant. I wanted to make it before dark. I did not want to find myself on the dark streets surrounded by criminals. Fortunately, I made while the sun was out. From the outside it looked normal, no different than the other restaurants. But it looked completely different on the inside. Luxury. Marble on the walls, brown leather seats, a waterfall, nicely dressed staff. I approached a waiter around my age who sent me to the kitchen to find one of the chefs. I tried to impress him. I praised the restaurant, his food, his knives. I praised him a lot. But I probably didn't try hard enough.

The situation was the same. I had to leave the restaurant. Before I left, he told me the reason for his disinterest. Why he was not interested in hiring me even though he had a job wanted poston the door. I had met their demands. I had the experience. I had references. The problem was coming from somewhere else.

Timothy was the problem. He had called all the restaurant owners in that neighborhood and told them what I had done a few years ago. How I damaged a couple of cars in Manhattan. Which is why I belonged among the renegades. What was there for me to even think about.

I did not expect anyone to have anything to do with me anymore. From being one of my friends, he had become my enemy.

I made the mistake of trusting him.

I still had not accepted it. So I kept looking.

I even asked again. I visited all the restaurants in the city. Italian, Chinese, Indian, Mexican. I always got turned down. The word spread fast. I continued until late into the night. No luck. Nobody wanted to give me a chance. No one gave me the opportunity to explain why I destroyed those cars. They did not understand that I had changed.

I would be okay with night work, minimum wage, unpleasant colleagues, stressful conditions, but with this?!

There was nothing else left than to find accommodation, or to spend time on the dangerous streets.

From my previous experience, I decided for the second option. I found a small motel near North Moore Street. I paid thirty dollars for the night. The endless silence was interrupted by the sound of the neon lights. The walls looked like they were from the jungle – the green on the walls caused by mold with such a horrible smell. I lied on the bed and was just thinking. I was thinking about my past.

I was thinking about my present. I was thinking about my future.

What will happen to me?

How would I get out of this situation?

I asked myself …

Fears and regrets dominated my thoughts. I was tired of this nervousness. Everything had happened so fast. Everything went wrong so fast. I really doubted that I could live a normal life like other people.

Be a favored one, have a good job, go out with friends, have a loving woman. You know, live the American dream, or live any dream at all. Instead, I just survived.

No joy in life, no pleasure in life.

Only troubles, sorrows, pain ...

In the morning I handed the keys from my room to the receptionist who was waiting for me to extend my stay, but that was not the case. Only a fool would have stayed there voluntarily. I went to try my luck somewhere else. I had to forget about working in a restaurant. So I tried shops, dry cleaners, laundromats. Without any success.

Surprisingly, all of them knew what I had done in my past. It seemed like all these people – who I had never even met before – knew my life better than I did myself! With no chance to find some job, I simply gave up.

I could have begged, I could have hoped, I could have prayed. Nothing worked. Timothy had made me a pariah.

"What now? What now?" I asked myself.

My ego did not allow me to go back to the shelter to ask the old lady for the possibility of living there again. I just couldn't do it. I needed to solve the situation. I regretted that I spent all my money on unnecessary clothes. I should have saved it. I should have kept it.

For my last fifty dollars, I could have spent the night in that cheap motel but without food. And then what?

Live onthe street, like I did with my mother?

A poor beggar?

Thinking about that dark period, a cold sweat overwhelmed me. Never ever again.

I could not allow my past to destroy my future. I could not let other people ruin my life.

I figured it would be best for me to get away from New York. Somewhere where people do not read the New York Post. Somewhere where people are not interested in the past.

Maybe Florida, or California, I was thinking.

Anyhow, I could not decide onan empty stomach. Important decisions require courage, which in my case meant the courage to spend what few dollars I had left. I could get a triple cheeseburger for three dollars atMcDonald's. I was hoping that I had just eaten my last meal in that damn city.

I asked the McDonald's cashier a simple question. Where do people to go to live a better life? *Clearly Los Angeles*, she answered me.

Los Angeles? For a while, I thought about it. Why not? There at least they have warm weather. No snow. No cold. Right,I had nothing to lose. Unbelievable – not just that I had vanquished my hunger, but I also got the answer I needed.

Thanks to this answer, I decided to go.

I hurried to the nearest bus station where I wanted to buy a one-way ticket to heaven. To Los Angeles.

I almost got a heart attack. They asked for one hundred and fifty-two dollars. One hundred and fifty-two dollars I did not have. My previous begging from strangers on the street for money had killed my pride. I lost all the barriers.

Feeling like I lost my conscience, I stopped the cars on the way. I stood in the middle of the road between those iron death traps on wheels, waving to the drivers hidden behind their windshields. They made their points quite clear. Honking. I tried to stop the passing cars, trucks, buses... no one stopped for me.

Except for the taxi drivers. They thought I needed to be taken somewhere. They were right.

I needed to be taken somewhere, but certainly not in a crazy expensive yellow taxi.

Maybe it was a coincidence and maybe not. The driver of a big blue truck, who almost ran me over, offered me a free ride. In the trailer, he was carrying some electronics to Los Angeles.

I had seen a lot of movies with truckers who murdered innocent hitchhikers. I would be an easy victim. In my current physical and psychical condition, a ten-year-old boy would have killed me. But the bus to Los Angeles was too much. And I couldn't afford to stay here. That truck is my only chance, I thought.

I got into the blue truck, next to a young trucker a little older than me. He looked like he could be thirty years old. After answering a couple of basic questions like:

Do you have a gun on you?

Are you running from the police?

Where's your mom?

Why Los Angeles?

He put on his safety belt, turned on some loud music on the radio and started off. We both did not talk much. Probably we didn't have much to talk about.

He stared ahead, eyes on the road, I looked around at the cars driving at high speeds.

Not only did I save one hundred and fifty-two dollars I did not have, but I was more comfortable than I would have been on the bus. The wide seat gave me more than enough room to sit and sleep.

Millions of people all over the world dream that one day, they can come to New York to live the American Dream. I just prayed that I would never have to go back to New York again.

I did not sleep much in that truck. My body is not made for such long periods of sitting. I was constantly looking for a better position to sit in. My butt hurt. My legs were stiff. A complete disaster.

We arrived in Los Angeles two days later in the morning. I thought it was about 5 am. The view from the passenger seat fascinated me. I did not know where to look. There was something exciting everywhere. Airplanes flew in the sky. Yachts sailed out at sea. Along the way, exotic cars were driving alongside us. All the houses looked so fancy. I had never seen so much sun in my whole life in New York. I felt like I was in a very luxurious Hollywood movie. The truck driver dropped me off at the bus stop. That heat woke me up. I looked at the city map on the board. I was lost. Literally.

Hundreds of options for where to go, and just one reason why to go there. I looked around. I chose one target. A tall skyscraper with a red banner on the hill behind which I followed. I was totally tired of walking through the empty streets accompanied by my own shadow. Occasionally, a barking dog cut the silence. From the quiet outskirts, I got to the city's busy center.

In New York, people were usually going to work at this time. In Los Angeles, people were returning home from parties.

I needed to relax. Get a bit of strength. I sat down on a wooden bench. After a minute I closed my eyes. My only companions were the singing birds in the surrounding trees. I was woken up by the noise of a car buzzing by on the road. I went to check my bag with my hand, but I was not able to find it. I opened my eyes and my bag wasn't there. Immediately I jumped off the bench and started looking for it. Next to the bench. Beneath the bench. Behind the bench. I could not find it anywhere. Someone had stolen it from me.

To be sure, I checked my wallet in my pocket, and I almost fainted. All my money was gone.

The thief left behind only my ID and one dollar.

Fucking one dollar!

I did not know whether I should cry or laugh.

By the way, I did both.

There was no one who could help me. I came here alone without anything. No family I could stay over with. No friends to support me. No arranged job to get me started.

Totally desperate, I stopped a police car patrolling down a nearby street. Dark bulletproof glasses protected the men of the law. With deep respect and a weird feeling, I knocked on passenger's window. A huge man in uniform came out of the car. He held his hand on his gun, ready to use it when needed. He checked me strictly and asked me what was happening. I took him to show where they had robbed me. I took no risks this time. I told him nothing but the truth about my forced departure from New York, about sleeping on the bench when they robbed me.

My story made an impression on that tough guy in the uniform. Not only did he buy me a hot dog and Cola, but he and his colleagues gave me some of their own money. Each one gave me ten dollars.

Words could not express my feeling of gratitude. I hugged them from the bottom of my heart.

Many people do not like cops. They judge them. They hate them. I was one of them. I honestly blamed myself for it at the time. The cops helped me many times. At elementary school, when they took me home in their car when I tried to commit suicide, and here in Los Angeles when I almost was stuck on the street without any money. They had done more for me than my father did. For me, these guys are heroes in uniforms. Real heroes. Every day they serve the people of this country. Each day they put their own lives at risk for the security of this country.

Before they got into their car, one of them advised me to be careful. *Young people like you, they see Los Angeles as the home of superstars. But they do not see that most of the city's population lives in poverty. People who struggle for survival do not take care of others. Trust me, I'm a cop. I know what I'm talking about.* He said.

Again, I thanked him for his help. He wished me luck, got into the car and left with the sirens turned off.

The rest of the day I spent on the beach watching people. I focused mainly on one group of people. On the women. Women in bikinis.

In the Bronx, I did not have the chance to see half-naked women. I had never even seen my own mom in her underwear. The view of those angelic creatures brought some peace to my mind. Rarely, some women noticed my attention and greeted me. I tried to pretend this was normal for me, but it really happened for the first time. I sat there like a rock with my cheeks blushing. I had never talked to a woman for more than one minute in my life. Besides my mom and the old lady from the shelter. I had no idea know what to talk about with them. After all, women are not interested in a loser, like I am.

The noise of the talking crowds was replaced by the loudly screaming seagulls flying in the sky like the black helicopters in Black Hawk Down. After sunset, almost everyone returned to their homes to their loving families. Outside were only those who enjoyed the nightlife and those who were fighting for their own lives.

I was not the weird one here. Someone different.

Next to me stood dozens of people just like me, people like you. Without a family. Without a home. Without any money. When I saw some of them just hanging out, I did not want to get any closer to them.

I preferred solitude. I chose one ordinary bench near Santa Monica. I lay on it with closed eyes, listening to the beautiful melody from a nearby restaurant. To be sure, I put my wallet in the back pocket of my jeans. If someone wanted to rob me a second time, he'd have to get me off the bench, which would definitely wake me up.

Maybe I should go to a cheap motel where I could sleep in a soft bed behind a locked door, but you know, nothing's cheap here in Los Angeles. I sacrificed the feeling of comfort. By saving money, I could buy some food. At that moment, the crazy idea of a huge pizza overflowing with ham entered my mind.

That night I did not sleep much. My conscience did not allow me. I had the urge to do something.

Something that would help me to stand on my own legs.

Something that would get me out of the streets.

First, I stopped by the arrogant owner of a souvenir shop. He said no, and I stopped looking for anything further. The fear of rejection was stronger than my desire for a better life. I did not want to listen to those words anymore –with every sentence ending in NO!

Eight days after my arrival here in Los Angeles and I was still living on the streets. It did not seem to be change for better over the next few days. Probably being a warrior in Los Angeles wouldn't be that bad. Due to the right weather conditions, it was nice to sleep in the open air.

That evening I needed to go out, to meet other people. If I didn't, I would probably go crazy.

A dark street opposite San Julian Park. This place looked like a gateway to the world where all the local warriors celebrated their escape from reality.

On that street, I saw a bunch of small groups.

Some groups were drinking cheap alcohol.

Some groups were using drugs.

Some groups were fighting.

And some groups were dancing around a burning trash bin.

Only one group, the last one on the corner, looked different. Peace and joy on their faces. Force and wisdom in their words. They stood there like bright stars in the dark sky.

These people radiated an incredible energy. Positive energy. They looked like clerks, wearing dark jeans and blue shirts. Nicely dressed, neat.

I did not have to say anything. They looked at me and invited me to join them. Their group.

I approached them with the expectation that I would be the one who just listens. But instead of listening, I talked. I talked because they asked me to share all the decisions from my past that had brought me to that dark street.

All the time I was talking, they were looking right into my eyes. They listened very carefully. They were there with me. When I shared all the decisions from my past, I felt an unbelievable relief for my soul. Then everyone thanked me for my sincerity, and as a sign of reverence shook my hand.

Hi, I'm Mike, I'm glad to meet you Tom.

Hi, I'm Bill, good to meet you Tom.

Hi, I'm Mike, but everyone calls me Double M, nice to meet you Tom.

For too long you have been carrying your issues inside yourself. The scars visible to the body are inspiring, but the scars hidden in the soul are devastating!

You lived in the belief that only terrible things are happening to you. Something like a family curse, from generation to generation.

Look at yourself, Tom!

You are so young, so healthy.

You have all your life ahead of you.

Don't feel sorry for yourself. Don' be sad that your life is not full of luxury and joy. Be thankful you got the chance to change things.

How, Mike? How do I change it?

You have to transform all your nightmares and worries into motivation, which will bringyou to a paradise full of love, joy, wealth and peace. What keeps you down now has to drive you forward. You lived life as a victim, because you believed that you were a victim. You accepted it. Your parents did not make you the Tom you are today. You have decided yourself to be the one you are today. If you are not happy with the life you're living right now, you have to start doing things differently than you have done so far.

I was thinking over these words. I just did not understand why Mike was telling me how to change my own life while he lived on the street like a warrior.

Why are you living a poor life in the dirt, Mike?

Why do you not change it? When you know how to do it.

I like you, Tom. You ask the right questions. You're a smart man. The truth is, I have no reason to change my life. Not just me, all of us: me, Bill and Double M have chosen this life. We did not meet coincidentally. Our lives have been matched by a disease. A terminal disease. Cancer. Together we fought in one room. Side by side like we were at war. Together we cried. Together we laughed. Many times, life tried to divide our paths, butwe did not give up. Together, we have faced all these challenges in life.

So you've already won against that horrible disease since you're not in the hospital anymore? For a moment he thought, he looked up at the sky as if he were looking for the answer.

I would like to tell you yes. But I think it's best if I tell you who we were and how we lived before we found ourselves on the street.

It will be my pleasure, Double M.

Ever since high school, I wanted to become a professional photographer. To photograph people, buildings, animals. To capture the world around me in all its beauty. To travel around the world. Get to know new people, new culture, new habits.

I'm sure you visited many interesting places, I said with excitement.

No, Tom. Unfortunately not. I allowed other people to determine my direction. My future. My parents lived an ordinary life. They had the same expectations for me. They wanted to have a normal son who had a stable job, cares about his parents, and spends all his time after work at home in front of the TV. A simple life without excitement or adventure. They kept giving me reasons why I could not become a professional photographer. How dangerous it is, how selfish it is to leave your family and not help them. How difficult is to live on this job. How unrealistic. From the beginning, I fought it, but eventually I gave up. I started to doubt myself. My abilities. My dreams. I was your age when I started doing what they thought was correct. I worked as a janitor at an elementary school. After work, I sat on the couch in front of the TV where I watched those boring sitcoms. Meanwhile, I was willing to help my parents around the house. I never had a girlfriend, no relationship with a woman. Because, according to my parents, it was selfish. My parents were cooking for me, buying my clothes, paying my bills. Despite my age, they treated me like a child. After the death of my parents, I was depressed for several months. Suddenly there was no one who could tell me what to do. No one to take care of me. The way I lived my life killed my responsibility, courage, self-confidence, creativity, vision, and independence. It went so far that I had to visit an expensive psychiatrist. Therapy helped me. Without it I probably would not have made it. Then, I decided to sell my parent's house and with this money go to Switzerland to photograph the nature I had dreamed of in my youth.

My plans were cut short by an unexpected event. Suddenly my health worsened. I had to be hospitalized at Heltcoin Clinical Research Hospital. The doctors diagnosed me with cancer. Despite expensive and lengthy treatment, there was no help for me. I have cancer at the fourth stage, which means no treatment can help me. No drugs. Simply put, I have cancer and I am dying. My lung cancer prevents me from getting on a plane and going to Switzerland to photograph the wilderness.

The second the plane takes off, my lungs would literally explode. So the money for the house I sold went to charity. I did it because there are many people in the world who are brave enough to fulfill their dreams.

Tom, please do not make the same mistake as I did. Go for your dreams, no matter what is going on around. You only live one life, you only get one chance. When the people around you scream no, cover your ears and keep going.

Pain in their hearts, tears in their eyes. But they continued, they considered it their duty to share with me their life stories.

Since my early childhood I knew I was extraordinary. Bill started.

The other guys my age wanted to be teachers, soldiers, or truck drivers. But I wanted to be something more than an average employee. I wanted to be a successful entrepreneur. I grew up as an only child with my old parents on a small farm. However, successful entrepreneurs do not live in poor poverty with old parents. That's why I moved to the city where millionaires live when I was eighteen.

To Los Angeles?

Yes, here. Right here in Los Angeles. I came here with nothing, determined to achieve something big. To be rich, famous, successful, significant. I found a well-paid job in one very luxurious club where the most famous personalities of this town would meet. Actors, singers, directors, politicians. I worked there as a bodyguard. Eighteen hours a day. I needed money for my own business. That drove me to work so hard. It gave me such an incredible amount of energy. It did not take long before I earned enough money. I had many options to invest it. I decided for something that I liked a lot. I opened my own fitness center on Wilshire Boulevard, right next to a FedEx office. Since the first day, my fitness center was always crowded. Everyone wanted to look good, even to be in top shape. I earned enough money. More than I needed. So I started buying new things. Very expensive things. Fast exotic cars, gold watches, diamond jewelry, crocodile leather boots. Living like a rock star. Until the financial crisis hit in 2007. People suddenly stopped going to my fitness center. They could not afford it. I naively believed that if I invested a lot of money into advertising, in new equipment, people would come back. I was wrong. Nobody came, and I had to leave too.

I lost everything. My income. My toys. My dream. My position in this city. I tried to get started again. I found the job

I left after a short time. But I could not listen to someone else's orders. To be a slave. I have been unemployed for many years. I sat on my butt at home, I blamed this state, the government, Obama. I neglected myself.

I looked terrible. I felt terrible. Then I started to drink. Only drinking made me happy. One day I got so drunk that I fell down the stairs right on my face and broke two teeth. I didn't have health insurance. I did not have the money for the treatment, the medication. So I left it like that, untreated. I did not pay any attention. This ordinary accident caused me unbearable pain. It was so bad I had to be hospitalized at Heltcoin Clinical Research Hospital. My diagnosis, fourth stage cancer. From my teeth it spread everywhere, into my lungs, my stomach, my brain. Instead of drugs, I got a bill. A fat bill for my stay in the hospital.

Don't make the same mistake as I did, Tom.

Take full responsibility for your own life, for your actions. Don't be naive thinking someone in this world, someone in this city will take care of you. That will not happen. Do not complain, do not go away, do not be sorry, do not blame others. When you are not satisfied with your life, close your mouth and work for a better life.

Sorry for my stupid questions, guys.

It's OK, Tom, it's really OK. You are still young. So young. You have to learn a lot of things.

I was also young and bold, Mike said.

We laughed like crazy. Our meeting was like a freaking Broadway show. Crying. Laughter. Every second a different emotion.

I come from a very good family. Mike continued. *We had everything we wanted. My parents worked for the government and I took care of my younger siblings after school. My sister and brother. I was the master of our house. I graduated from a local school with honors. Then I left New York for Los Angeles. I chose Los Angeles because I got a scholarship here.*

I was among the best students. My long hours of studying were rewarded. I spent all my free time studying, something that most people considered to be crazy. They wanted me to have a little excitement in my life. So they convinced me to join them one evening. I tell you, this party was incredible. I met a wonderful girl there. She looked so beautiful. I was attracted to her, she was attracted to me. I knew that. Because my roommate was her friend and she told him. I bought some new clothes. I started to workout. I started using cologne. I wanted to make an impression on her. I imagined how we would live together. One for another. I was head-over-heels in love. I could not sleep. I was constantly thinking about her. She gave me an incredible energy. I felt like it was some kind of drug.

How did you ask her out, Mike?

Truth is Tom, I never did. I wanted to invite her on a date, but in the right place atthe right situation at the right time. And while I was waiting, someone else invited her on a date. She is now married to that man and has three beautiful children. Tasha, Patrick, Gregg.

I did not even have the chance to express what I feltfor her. Sadly, this hasn't happened to me once. At twenty-six I started working at a bank. I liked the job, but my dad had a problem. A big problem. Because in the past the bank had taken his sister's home.

He tried to convince that I had made a mistake. He insisted that I give a resignation letter to the bank. We did not agree, which led to anargument. Since then, we have not been talking for at least three years. But I could not continue that nonsense. Over time, I realized how stupid we were. So I decided to make the relationship up with him.

I wanted to apologize to him on his birthday, on December 20. Unfortunately, my father did not live to that date. On July 17, he died of cancer. I felt so horrible when I saw him for the first time after three years, lying in a coffin ...

I regretted how I treated him. After his funeral, my mom advised me to visit a doctor. She was worried about my health.

My grandfather also died of cancer. I did not listen to her. At my work, the position of Bank Director was available. I had dreamed of that position for many years. In any case, I could not leave it to anyone else. I started working sixteen hours a day, including weekends. I participated in every meeting that took place. I did not have time to visit some doctor. I felt healthy. Four months later, my hard work paid off. It was worth it. I got the position as the director of the bank. My enthusiasm and joy disappeared very soon. I regularly had stomach issues, started disliking all food, and I lost weight. I thought it was due to stress at my job. So I took a few days off for vacation. Nevertheless, my health problems persisted.

I had to go to the hospital. There I was diagnosed with the same disease that killed my father and my grandfather. Colon cancer. The doctors told me that if I came earlier, the treatment would have helped me.

Please do not make the same mistake like I did, Tom.

Do not wait for the right time. It will never be the right time. If you want to do something, do it. No matter how, no matter where, no matter who.

Do not delay anything. When your inner voice says tomorrow, close your eyes and do it now. Right now.

So you all met in the same hospital, in the same room?

Yes, Tom.

Why did you leave?

You know, your surroundings are key to your life. You remember that you enjoyed watching movies, right?

Yes, Mike, I loved to watch movies, but I can't do this when I'm on the street.

I suppose you were nice, peaceful, and non-violent guy, but when you turned on the television and watched a movie about violence, for example, The Godfather, your behavior changed. Suddenly you wanted to be a dangerous, respected, bad guy with weapons under his belt. Do you agree with me, Tom?

Yes. You got it right.

Now imagine what happens to you when you spend the entire day hanging with people who just lie on the bed waiting for their death to come. The doctors and nurses around you regret speaking with you because they know you're dying. This place took our energy, joy, and faith. If we stayed there, we would be the same as these people. We would just lie down on the bed and wait for the last breath of our lives.

I understand now, but why did you stay on the street?

You know, all our lives we were slaves.

Slaves?

Yes, slaves to society.

We had to follow the rules set by other people. Do what the other people do. Manage the way others behave. Live the lives of other people. Even Bill as an entrepreneur had to follow the rules of other people. Now, on these streets nobody tells us what, how, when, why, or where. We do what we want. It's freedom. Freedom holds us here. In the past, when I was healthy and lived a normal life, I felt poor. I felt poor even though

I was a well-paid director of the bank.

I saw people wear better clothes than I wore.

I saw people living in better homes than I had.

I saw people driving better cars than I did.

I saw people eat better meals than I ate.

The world around me has forced me to feel poor. On these streets among the homeless, one who owns the shiny toys of the outside world isn't rich. Here, to be rich is to live a rich life within their own, like us. We are happy here. Really happy.

Bill, Double M agreed with Mike. Their sincere smiles confirmed it.

The first rays of the sun had started to hit the dark street, which meant the end of our meeting. Mike, Bill, and Double M left on their way, while I set off in my own direction. Straight to the city.

This time I did not watch the women in bikinis. I was not going to close my eyes until I found some work. I will not close my eyes until I found work. I was repeating it over and over again. I asked people in their shops, I asked people on the street. I asked people in cars stuck at a traffic light. Their answers had not changed. Mostly they said NO, but my attitude changed. I did not listen to their rejections. I continued on. Just like Double M, a few hours ago.

On Paloma Street, I met a large green dump truck that just stood on the edge of the road while guys in orange uniforms were taking the trash away.

I stopped beside them. I asked them what I needed to do so I could do what they do.

Why aren't you in school boy? one of them asked me.

Why are not you in the office? I asked him back.

You are a funny young man. If you really have an interest in doing this work, get your butt in the car. Our "lady" is already full. We'll take it to the dump and blow it all out, and we'll get you in the company. There you will find what you are looking for.

Thank you, guys.

No! We thank you. I will finally be able to take some time off. Today's people are not interested in doing this type of work. It's not good enough for them.

OK, by the way, I'm Tom …

Oh my God. The craziest ride of my life. These guys are total mad men. I was laughing my ass off the whole time. When I was dropped in front of the company, I had to walk along a long, straight road. Besides me, no one else was there. They screwed with me. They drove their truck slowly behind me, and when I did not expect it, they honked loudly. I screamed and jumped to the side of the road. I heard their laughter even through the unbearable noise of the car. Then they turned and drove away…

A little shaky from that nice joke, I walked into an old building. Inside I could only hear my own footsteps, nothing else. I knocked on the door of the "stinking" boss. I did not waste my time. I stepped inside. I said hello to the boss and I shared that I wanted to work for him.

Not tomorrow, not next month, but now.

Right now.

Slow down, boy, I'm an older man. Let's take a look at it.

From the table he picked a piece of paper. Then he continued.

Okay, boy, I got the job for you.

Super, thank you, sir.

Now listen carefully to me! I do not care what you do during the day. Are you drinking beer at the local bar? Alright, I do not care. Are you selling marijuana to young students? Alright, I do not care. Are you meeting up members of a gang? Alright, I do not care. I only care about one thing! What you do at night. Do you understand me?

Yes, boss. I understood.

You are starting next Thursday.

You will make night shifts from 6 pm to 6 am everyday, from Monday to Sunday. Here are the keys to your locker, you'll find your uniform and shoes there. If you destroy them or lose them, you will not get new ones.

Thank you, boss. You will not regret it, I promise!

I felt such a sense of joy. I jumped out of pure enthusiasm. I did it! I did it! I did it!

This success deserved a reward. I deserve a reward. I bought a big ice cream and hamburger on the beach. I did not care that my wallet had only seventeen dollars left. I got a job, which meant a regular income.

No more worries about money.

I had to share my success with my new friends. The clock on the sidewalk showed 3 pm. I hoped they would be there during the day, not just at night. I was lucky. Mike, Bill, Double M, stood in the same place on the same street as yesterday. They had already seen my wide smile.

What's up with you, Tom? You look very happy.

You're right Double M, I feel very happy. Thank you! Today I found my job. I'm starting next Thursday. I am very grateful to you. When you told me your life stories and gave me your advice, I took them to my heart. Without you I could not have done it.

You know, we knew you are a smart boy. We were expecting you here. Yesterday you told us something. Something about your life. In that rush full of trouble and fear, you had forgotten a very important thing. You have your birthday today. Today you are nineteen years old. Happy birthday, Tom.

What? I couldn't understand, how did you know it?

Yesterday you showed us your ID card, the one where you had long hair in the picture. Do you remember?

Yes, Double M, I remember.

So I found it. That's not all. We have a gift for you here. A book. Together with Mike and Bill, we bought it for you. The book is about a young man with two dads. They both taught him something different. The one he chose to listen to influence his life, his future.

I really appreciate it, thank you guys. What else can I do for you?

Please don't worry. Your presence, Tom, is the most valuable thing for us to enjoy. I know you are very excited about your success, but have you thought about where you'll get the money for food?

Of course. Now I have the money for six hot dogs, which will last till next Thursday.

And then?

Then I'll buy more hot dogs from my paycheck.

I hate to say so, but you will receive your first payout after one month.

What? Why didn't he tell me this?

They had no reason to. It's normal, how the system works everywhere, throughout the whole world…

My enthusiasm immediately disappeared.

What will I eat?

How do I make money now?

Not in a month …

Look around you. You live in America. In the place of unlimited possibilities and wealth. The longer you stand idle, the longer your problem will last. Open your eyes. Watch carefully and find what you are looking for. Trust me!

Aclassic birthday. Something always has to go wrong. Like Black Hawk Down, I circled on the ground and looked for some opportunity. Stealing was not under consideration anymore. I will no longer lower myself to such a level. I promised myself. Surprisingly, my book only caused problems. It fell twice out of my hands and I had to look for it on the sidewalk. How can I read a book when I would soon be starving? Reading won't feed me.

So I hid it inside my jeans. Only there was it safe.

I continued with my search. I looked like a tourist admiring the local sights. I was looking everywhere possible. But I did not see anything. I didn't find anything. Only a waste of time, I thought. I was disappointed, and I sat down on a bench and looked straight at to my shoes.

Then, when I least expected it, I suddenly saw it. All the time I had it right before my eyes. Unbelievable.

I ran into the nearest store to buy some pencils and a few pieces of white paper. It cost me less than two dollars.

I went back and sat down on the edge of the sidewalk, where most people were walking past. The busiest place I could find. It reminded me of the times when I was sitting in New York City on the edge of the sidewalk, but I sat down here with a completely different purpose. I chose one object and I started to draw. I finished the drawing and put it down next to me. From a limited budget, I could not afford to waste paper. One drawing, as proof of my abilities, should be enough.

To my surprise, people liked it. Some praised my drawing, some embraced me and some even asked to draw them. I drew a young married couple. A freaky dog. A baby with her mother. I received four dollars for one drawing. In less than three hours, I earned sixteen dollars.

The easiest money in my life. Why did not I think of this sooner? My enthusiasm and joy were starting to come back.

Double M did not disappoint me. I live in a country with unlimited possibilities and wealth. Again, I quickly escaped to stock up in the store. This time I bought dozens of paper.

I sat in the same place. Another married couple, I think from China, asked me for adrawing. Not just that. They recorded me drawing. I just did not know whether they were recording me out of regret or admiration. In any case, it did not matter to me. The important thing was they paid me.

The rest of the day I spent drawing on the pavement. Overall, I earned twenty-one dollars.

A decent budget. I could imagine what to do with it. Today I had done more than my last eighteen years of life. I had the energy to draw all day. Only other people had no reason to stay out all day. When only the night time warriors were crossing the pavement, I called it a day.

On the way back to the bench, I did not go to share with Mike, Bill or Double M how I had solved my problem.

I wanted to be alone. Lonely. To enjoy that amazing feeling. I closed my eyes and was flying in the clouds.

I woke up in the morning, later than usual. I felt totally exhausted because of the day before. I checked my wallet, book and tools. Nobody had stolen anything.

I was ready to continue. I sat again in my lucky spot, at the edge of a path and proudly showed my drawings around me. But this time, not just one amateur drawing, but three by areal artist. I was sitting there over many hours without moving at all. People passed by, looked at me, looked at my drawings and then continued on. Since the early morning I only sold one drawing. Not good, I said. I must change something. Immediately. Otherwise I am done here.

I got up, looked around.

I looked for something, anything.

Then I got an idea. Again.

That shop where I bought the papers, they also sold a big wooden painters stand. Instead of the canvas, I put a large piece of paper on it. Huge drawings, huge interest, big money. It could work. It must work! I find that big things are big money. I paid almost everything I had. When I picked it up, I came to see that all those hot dogs had not given me much power. I took it away from the shop with much difficulty and I put it in its new place.

A few meters further. Next to the ice cream stall.

A smart decision. The ice cream man served his customers, who then passed by me and my drawings.

My drawings were amazing. People stood in line like they were waiting for LeBron James's signature.

I drew everything. People, their animals, even their cars. Normally when people looked at me, my head was shaking from nervousness. Now, I was standing here completely relaxed. I was used to those looks by now. I took it as part of my performance. I stopped drawing when the last piece of paper was out of stock in the shop. The store vendor did not understand what I was doing with so much paper. After counting all the money I made today for drawing, I couldn't believe it was true.

In my hands, I held two hundred and twenty-five US dollars. Besides a feeling of intense joy, I had a dilemma.

What should I buy with this money first?

A meal?

Accommodation at a motel?

Clothes?

I chose one of each. First, I bought a belt because my jeans were too big. I also bought a backpack, for my book and the food I would carry to work. Then I was looking for accommodation. Cheap accommodation. There was no choice. Almost all the available motels in this city were already occupied. Only when I offered more money to the receptionist was she motivated to find a room for me. My new home became a motel on Central Ave. The view from the window was terrible, but at least I had hot water and a soft bed. To stock up I bought peanut butter and a couple of sandwiches. I was sure that I wouldn't suffer the next few weeks. Finally I bought a big bacon pizza. My first fresh, non-frozen pizza.

I did the same the following days. I went to my happy place, and I bought some vanilla ice cream from the ice cream shop because the owner allowed me to have my wooden drawing stand so close to his stall. I started to draw. I got the paper. I ate. I packed the stand. I went back to the motel and calculated the money I earned.

This is how I continued mydays until Thursday. With one difference, I finished drawing on that day at lunch time. I had to arrive to my new job on time. BeforeI left, I drew a portrait from the depths of my heart. A portrait of Mike, Bill, Double M, and Me. I bought them a pizza. The biggest and the most expensive. I wanted to share my success with them. I did not have a problem with the money. My drawings in four days earned me more than four hundred and fifty dollars.

A decent amount for a warrior.

On the dark street, they looked at me like I was a holy saint. Their hands were reaching out to me like zombies. Not today guys, not today …

I gave the box of pizza to only one group of guys.

My dear friends. The cheese pizza pleased them, but my drawing was the thing that touched them.

Tom, tell us how you got the idea to draw.

You know Bill, I had it the whole time right in front of my eyes. I just didn't pay attention.

Opposite the bench where I sat, there were two warriors. Both looked similar. They wore old, ripped clothes. They had stout faces. One only sat there sadly, probably waiting for a miracle to save him, while the other was singing like he was on stage. With passion, energy, enthusiasm. People only gave money to one of them. The singer. I'm a terrible singer, but I'm great at drawing. So I used it.

Mmm. Remarkable.We're proud of you.

These warm words warmed my heart. I did not stay long. The service of my homeland was waiting for me. I came to the company earlier than the others. I put on my new orange uniform. It fit perfectly. I sat in front of the mirror for a few minutes. I looked at all the different angles. From a distance. From nearby. From the left. From the right. The other guys were coming in, which meant I had to interrupt my little catwalk. Otherwise they would have caught me in a delicate situation.

I sat down on a stool, pulled my heavy metal toe shoes, and waited impatiently …

There were fifteen more guys coming to the night shift. Everyone greeted me and shook my hand. As they changed into their uniforms. Two of them asked me to follow them. At that moment I was excited. But I couldn't bear the smell any longer. Some guys smelled like my two-week-old socks. We got to the dump truck. Yuri, my colleague showed me how to dispose of the trash and which push buttons I should press. It looked simple. We jumped in to "the old lady" and set off for the streets. I didn't talk much. In my head I was repeating how to dispose of the waste and what buttons I should press. I did not want to mess it up. We stopped at the edge of the city. With Yuri I stepped out, then we moved to the rear of the truck.

I stood on the right side, Yuri on the left.

From the beginning, I was nervous. I was afraid I'd fall from the driving car, but then I found out I had nothing to worry about. If he could do that, Yuri with his wounded leg, I could handle it as well. I assured myself. From that moment on I started to enjoy it.

The breeze in my face, stars in the night sky, lights from the buildings, music from the nightclubs. Something indescribable. And the dirt? The bad smells?

Nothing terrible. In the cloakroom it was going to smell much more …

I finished the first day at work, it went by so fast. When I returned to motel, I ate peanut butter sandwiches and set out to draw in my happy place. I expected other things to happen during this day. I stood there tired, off mood, low energy, doing something. Those heavy boots made for bloody bruises on my legs. After painting the second portrait I called it a day. With my aching legs, I slowly walked back to the motel. I lay down the bed. I immediately fell asleep. I could do nothing more.

I woke up with a jolt as my alarm clock started ringing at5 am. I got dressed and went to work. Starting it all again. I was very nervous, because these blisters on my feet were causing me great pain. I almost cried. But I stopped my tears only because of my colleagues. If they would see me crying, they would certainly start teasing me. I got in the car, we went to pick up Yuri a few minutes away, then we took it to the streets. Today I wasn't thinking about how to dispose of the waste, I already knew. Instead I listened to Yuri.

He told me about his life. About how he and his family had run from poverty in Russia. About his two daughters studying at a San Francisco High School. Of course, he told me about his wife Veronika, which caused him many more headaches.

After work, he invited me to his home for a shot of Russian vodka. Thankfully, I rejected him. I would not let myself get caught into that trap. I simply would not! I've seen what alcohol can do to people and their families. Never in my life would I drink a drop of that crap. I will never drink it in my life.

As usual, I came home exhausted from work. In no mood to do anything. And I did not even want to go out into the heat where I would draw under the hot sun. For sure, I counted all my money. Luckily, I had enough money to make it to the first payday. No need for drawing, I'm going to survive without it, my justification was easy this time.

My life continued in the same pattern. Every night work, and during the day sleep. Finally, after a tough month,I received my paycheck. Much bigger than I expected, which made me even strongly believe that I had made the right decision to stop drawing.

I bought my first smartphone with my paycheck.

A space gray iPhone.

I sacrificed some hours of sleep for fun. In my case, using free Wi-Fi. I discovered many interesting things on the Internet. I registered for Instagram and Facebook where I could look at other people's photos. I was impatiently waiting for new photos from Dan Bilzerian. On YouTube, I watched funny videos. This smartphone replaced my need to be in someone else's company. After work I did not need to be among the people.

I made an exception only for Christmas.

That day I got off at work. So I went to visit my friends. I had not seen them for a long time, and I was totally missing them. When I came to the place where we had shared our moments, on that dark street, I only saw other warriors there. A lot more warriors than ever before. During Christmas, all people need to be together. Surrounded by family, friends. I wanted it too.

I stood at the end of the street, but I did not see the guys that I was looking for. I searched for them on the side streets. I could not find them anywhere. I stayed there waiting for many hours, hoping for them to appear. They did not come. But I wanted to meet them. Talk to them. Spend this day with them.

An old warrior came to me on an old rusty wheelchair and asked me who I was waiting for. I'm waiting for my friends Mike, Bill and Double M, I answered him. We always spent the evenings here. Do you know them?

Yes, boy. They told me about you. You are the talented cartoonist, right?

Yes, that's me. Where can I find them? I really want to see them.

You know, two weeks ago I was here with them. We enjoyed some delightful Turkish coffee. That night Bill did not feel well. The next morning, Bill didn't wake up. He died. Cancer killed him. When I found out, I just went for Mike and the Double M. Unfortunately I came too late. They left for Bill. Mike, Double M, they committed suicide. They jumped under the train. They promised each other that they would leave this world together. They kept their promise. I'm sorry, boy.

Broken by this news, I stumbled to the ground. I was able only to lie there. Tears were running down my cheeks. Why? Why? It can't be true. It can'tbe true. You're lying! You are lying to me!

I'm so sorry, boy. So sorry.

I wanted to tell them so many things. I wanted to show them so many things. But I could not. I had the time to meet them when they were still alive. Only when they died did I really realize how I had left them. How selfish I was.

I should have been that day with them. I closed my eyes and remembered having good times with these guys.

They were more than my friends.

They were like the older brothers I never had.

Mike, Bill, Double M, I'll never forget you.

Thanks to you, I got off the street. Thanks to you, I'm living a better life. Thank you so much for teaching me such important things.

The book they gave to me sat all this time unread on my nightstand. It's time to uncover the secrets of a book that I should have uncovered months ago. Reading the book seemed to me like traveling back in time. I fully recognized the author's opinion. I found myself often thinking, exactly, that's true. It's a shame I did not have another dad, a rich dad, as he did. I read the first two chapters. Then I quit. That's enough for today, my eyes are shutting. I was tired from working. I went to bed, where I tried to sleep. My thoughts did not allow me to sleep. I was still thinking about that book.

I took it from the table and continued reading. Every chapter forced me to reflect on my own life. To reassess what I want to achieve in my life. To be a slave, or to be a lord. After reading the book, I felt fuzzy. Why did no one tell me? Why did no one show it to me? This should be taught in schools instead of the needlessness of war, history that happened hundreds of years ago and no one cares about it.

Everything in this book made sense to me.

It all fits.

Money does not work for me, I work for money.

I have a monthly income from my job, but if I stopped working, I would lose it.

I have a couple of expenses and no assets.

I do not save any money, I spend all of it.

I was doing exactly what my poor parents did.

Every day, I work hard for other people's dreams.

I must change it. I must make something out of my life.

I do not want to live as my parents lived. I like my job, but now I was finding that there are other ways to make money.

I started to invest in myself. I bought dozens of books about business, about success. I was determined to become my own boss with my own rules. I really believed that I had the power to live the life I want to live. A life filled with love, joy, and richness. From the bottom of my heart I believed in it. Books became my passion. I did not spend my precious time scrolling through photos on Instagram, playing GTA San Andreas, or watching TV. Instead, I was just reading Forbes magazine and books and watching motivational videos on YouTube.

The more books, articles, and stories I read, the more I got crazy thinking about my own business.

It's not hard, just have a good idea and people will pay for it, I assured myself.

I'll make millions.

I'll own a luxury mansion in Hollywood.

I'll drive a Ferrari.

I will wear a tailor-made Italian suit.

I'll travel around the world in a private jet.

I'll be a rich person who actually means something.

I wanted it now. Not in ten years. Now!

I was so strong, so clear with this idea of an exciting life in my head ...

I felt the wind in my hair while driving my red Ferrari. I saw all those guys envious of my luxury lifestyle, my relationship with Victoria's Secret models. I heard the vast applause of the audience while I was receiving the awardas entrepreneur of the year. I put my ideas on paper. I drew cars, watches, houses. All the things that I would soon own. There was just one problem. I had no idea what to do. I did not know any successful entrepreneurs.

I had to search for it in books, on the Internet. I typed into Google: "best business to start." How to Make One Million Dollars. I read advice, experience, stories. Apparently, the best way to make millions is to sell something on the Internet. Some businessmen sell jewelry, dresses, or furniture.

Some entrepreneurs sell eBooks, tutorials. I chose women's fashion. Handbags to be precise.

The poor and the rich. Young and old. Unemployed and employed. Single and married. Every woman carries a handbag. It would be easy to sell.

I started looking for entrepreneurs who got rich by selling women's handbags and I read their strategy, stories, and advice. Anything that could help me. The hardest part was to find acompany that would produce them for me. I contacted handbag manufacturers in Asia with years of experience. A few days later I received the answer with an offer: the minimum order quantity is five thousand pieces. Unit price for fifteen bucks. When I figured it out I almost broke the display on my smartphone.

I'm not the son of the president. I could no longer consider producing in Asia. They were asking for crazy money. I had not even started yet, and yet I had to change my whole strategy or start another business. I need to sell in small quantities but with a high profit. I Googled a bit. Then I found it. I would sell handbags as planned. Only with one difference, I will sell luxury handbags to rich women. They're still spending crazy money on their handbags. This time, I did not contact any manufacturers in Asia. I contacted craftsmen in Italy who produce handmade leather goods for other luxury companies. I sent five emails. Within twenty-four hours I got two answers with offers. The minimum order quantity is ten pieces. The cost per piece is nine hundred dollars + transport. I'll need ten thousand dollars to start a business.

This meant no spending money, just saving and hard work. Pity I did not have anyone to talk to it about.

Bill would help me, he was an entrepreneur.

He would advise me.

So I set a goal to earn ten thousand dollars in the shortest time possible.

In my case, it took a never-ending fourteen months. Fourteen months full of restrictions.

Such hard work.

Buying only the cheapest food.

No entertainment.

No unnecessary spending.

Simply put, no pleasure, no fun.

Every morning, before I got out of bed I closed my eyes and imagined what it would be like when I became a successful entrepreneur. Every morning! This idea forced me to get out of bed even though I was totally tired and overworked. This idea forced me to say NO to the people who were asking me out to pool parties. This idea forced me to keep on going, to continue even though I wanted to give up.

Guys at my age spend their money on a new Mercedes, exotic holidays, cheap women. Just to live a rich life in the present. While I saved every penny to invest in a business, which will make me live a rich life for the rest of my life.

Yes, I had the opportunity to borrow money from the bank. It would save me months of hard work and limitations, but I could not do it.

Because the bank had taken our apartment in the Bronx.

At work, I resigned with a thirty-day notice period. My colleagues considered me a fool because I was one of the best. I did not listen to them. I did not listen to their speeches. They gave just me another reason to become a successful entrepreneur and to prove that they were wrong. I can prove to all the people who judged me and bullied me that I am better than they are.

I can do it! I can do it! I can do it!

I solved my lack of money. I needed to finish a few more important things. Like the actual design of the handbags. Using my creativity and a little inspiration from the best luxury handbags, I did it in two days.

Choosing a business name was more complicated. Far more complicated. I was thinking, combining, translating. None of them seemed fit. The names I wanted to use had all been used by someone else already. After four days I stopped. I used what I could have started with from the beginning. I chose my own name as the business name.

At the end, I did the most important thing.

I started my own company. My dream was fulfilled. Later, I found out that as CEO of my own company I also must have my own bank account. I compared the terms of different banks. I decided for Air City Bank. Their conditions suited my business – open and run an account for free if your monthly turnover exceeds thirty thousand dollars. I expected far more than just thirty thousand dollars. The most unpleasant things, the bureaucracy, were over.

The last days of work passed slowly. Very slowly. My body stood in the back of the dump truck, but my mind was somewhere else. In a better and more beautiful place.

Wednesday morning, 06:02 am. Finally!

I'm no longer a slave. I'm free. I am my own boss.

I sent the handbag design to Italian craftsmanship.

I checked my email inbox again and nothing.

I checked it again and still nothing. I tried about another seven times. I did not get one single reply. I'm rushing to do everything as soon as possible, while a small businessman in Italy is testing my patience. The rest of the day was spent in bed waiting for a stupid email from an Italian. No answer. He was not able to write back the whole day. My unanswered questions circled around in my head. Maybe the email got flagged as spam? Is he not interested in working together? Or did he forget that we had agreed together fourteen months ago? I could not explain it.

I finally received an answer in the afternoon that next day. My worries were gone. Finally. I was so impatient. I opened it and read: *Hi Tom, I'm busy now. I looked at your design, it looks perfect. The price will be somewhat lower than I expected. About five hundred dollars a piece. + transport. I just want to ask if you want a logo printed as well?*

Because I cannot see a logo there. Looking forward to your answer. Yours sincerely …

Oh my God. The logo! How could I forget? I ran to the nearest graphics studio. Two days! They'll have it done in two days. You've got to be kidding me. Am I the only one who works so fast? Or does no one care about me? After two days of wasted time waiting for the logo, I received an SMS message. It's done. A miracle. I paid eighty dollars for the two ordinary words. I would have done it better myself in Word. But I rather kept the complaints for myself. Now was the time that I could not afford unnecessary problems. I immediately sent the logo to the Italian along with the order.

Ten pieces of cow leather handbags.

Five pieces in brown, five pieces in black. I also added the delivery address with the invoice request. I read one article where they recommended that start-up entrepreneurs register a trademark. I had not thought about it for a long time. And I had just registered my own trademark like all big successful companies. Soon I will be among them.

This time I got an email back suspiciously fast. The Italian sent me an invoice and a confirmation with the expected delivery time of three weeks. I took it positively. Handmade goods take a lot of time. I checked the billing data and sent $5,300 to a foreign account via Internet banking. So simple. Just a few clickson the display.

I thought three weeks would go by fast. I was wrong. Suddenly I had so much free time and nothing to do.

I could not continue without my handbags. I began to feel lonely. For almost two years I had spent half a day away from the motel. I worked with Yuri and the other guys. I missed those moments of laughter, fun. I missed those people. Even the ones I did not like. I knew what to do and how to do it. I did not care about anything else. From 6 pm to 6 am I only moved dirty trash cans to the dump truck, I pressed the button and I put the empty trash cans back.

Now it's different. Not a single book wrote about what it was like to be alone for everything. Without any support. Without any certainty. I had been fighting these feelings for exactly two weeks.

When my order arrived I was caught by excitement. I carefully unpacked a large brown box and took my handbags out. Real pieces of art. They had managed to exceed my expectations. That leather. That sewing. That quality. Perfect. The Italian did a really good job. Now I was finally able to visit the photo studio. These handbags had to look really good if I wanted to sell them.

That's why I had them shot by the best photographer in the city. Meanwhile, as I admired his work, he sat down and photographed every handbag. When he finished, he also offered me the creation of a website. I agreed. I left it in his hands. The photos and the website were done the next day. This guy deserved the money. It looked luxurious.

The ordinary life of ordinary Tom is over. Let's sell!

On my smartphone, I reviewed the website, prices, business terms, contact, and photos. Nothing was missing. Everything worked. Ready to ship the first handbags. I set the price according to other luxury companies. For each piece sold, I would get $2,600. After deducting production costs and shipping, I'm going to be earning exactly $1,974.

I had to sell five hundred and seven pieces to become a millionaire.

Only five hundred and seven pieces formed the line between poor me and rich me.

I can do it!

The first day since the sales started, nothing happened. No emails, no orders.

The second day since the sale started, nothing happened. No emails, no orders.

The third day since the sale started, nothing happened. No emails, no orders.

The fourth day since the sale started, nothing happened. No emails, no orders.

The fifth day since the sale started, nothing happened. No emails, no orders.

The sixth day since the sale started, nothing happened. No emails, no orders.

The day after the sale started, nothing happened.

No emails, no orders.

On the eighth day I got my first email.

Unfortunately, not the email I was expecting.

The Italian wrote me. He asked me when I would order another round of handbags. I did not reply. I was ashamed.

I was afraid of what he was thinking of me. All of the handbags delivered a couple of weeks ago were still in the box. Unsold. I did not understand.It did not make any sense.

I had the perfect product.

I had a website with PayPal payment button.

I had quality photos.

I had a registered trademark. I had prices like other luxury companies. I had a legal company.

I had a manufacturer from Italy.

Where is the problem?

I called the photographer to request a trial purchase on my website. It worked. The website is fine. Damn... maybe the rich women are just busy... This was the only reasonable explanation I could come up with.

The nightmares of every businessman had entered my life. I got the first checks together from my bank account statement. I opened the envelope from the bank and my stomach twisted into knots. Overall, I had spent $6,120 in two months. Account balance of $4,003.

What the hell?

Where did I spend so much money and for what? Unbelievable.

I opened a second envelope with my checks.

The bank asked me for a hundred dollars to run the business account. The next check shocked me. I had to pay four hundred dollars for last month and another four hundred dollars this month.

What?

I did not want to pay four hundred dollars every month for health insurance! I did not need it. I called angrily the number listed in the envelope. I asked them to cancel my health insurance, saying that I had not signed up for it. The operator really tested me. She had a lot of questions.

I provided my personal data, which she subsequently verified.

Are you Mr. Tom Seed? Yes. I am Mr. Tom Seed.

In the system I see you did not pay for the last month, please pay it as soon as possible.

Then she continued.

You as a business owner are legally obliged to pay health insurance every month. Do you have any more questions about it, Mr. Seed? No! Well thank you for your time.

Full of fear, I immediately paid it.

Anxiety overwhelmed me. I started to doubt myself. I had been doing business for two months and I had not sold anything yet. I had not earned anything yet. I only spent over $7,000. Almost all the money I saved for eighteen months. I was wondering what to do next.

Did it make sense to continue with this business? Should I give up?

Should I start selling something else?

If I gave up, it would not be too reasonable. I had been investing a lot of money. If I went on, I could find someone who could help me with that.

When it all looked like I was giving up on this idea, something happened that offered the opportunity to change my situation. I received an email from a blogger who works as an editor at one online luxury magazine. She was interested in writing an article about my handbags. Without hesitation, I agreed. I sent her high-resolution photos and some details. She replied at the speed of light.

Hi Tom, thank you for the photos. They look great. When I finish the article, I will send it to you. I wish you an amazing day, best regards ...

I prepared my handbags for shipping. I put some paper with a handwritten thank you note for the purchase into each one. Then I wrapped them in the gold wrapping paper and placed them close to the door.

I was expecting a huge amount of demand. I called the photographer again to demand a new design of the website. This time, I need a very luxurious design. I agreed with his price. He was about to change it immediately.

Great mood. Good news. Finally, a reason to cheer a bit.

It took one week to write an article about my handbags. The title of the article contained my name, Tom Seed. I was so proud of myself. So honored. People from all over the world could see my name, my handbags in the magazine.

I snapped a picture with smartphone and uploaded it proudly to my Facebook account. The publication of this article helped me become more visible. I regularly received offers from bloggers who wanted my handbags in exchange for uploading photos to their Instagram account. I refused these offers politely. I'm not a fool, willing to give somebody a gift. I'm not a charity. I am an entrepreneur.

Occasionally, I also got interview requests. I ignored most of them except one. One journalist invited me to lunch. I should have prepared for the answers to her questions. Most of them looked normal. Where are your handbags made or who is your idol. Only one question forced me to think.

The question was: *When will your handbags also be available in department stores.*

I did not know how to answer this question. I was planning to sell five hundred handbags through my website, and with this $1 million to enjoy life like Charlie Harper. Nothing more.

None of my own boutiques. No distributor. No party. I Googled how to get my handbags into shopping malls. But I did not find much. They just wrote about the need to contact the purchasing department. I visited the sites of luxury shops in shopping malls and wrote them emails. I needed it as soon as possible, so I called them too. I called a department store here in Los Angeles.

Send us information by email, sir, we will look at it and we will contact you if we are interested.

I heard this same reply at least fifteen times.

They did not understand the situation I was in at all. The journalist's interview was approaching. Without a reply that I could not come do it. I would be like a total amateur. I also called outside of Los Angeles, to Miami. There I listened to the same information over and over again. I think one lady heard the despair in my voice and gave me an opportunity. *Come in three days with your handbags to our shopping mall.* She told me.

Yes, Yes, Yes! Perfectly on time for my interview.

I bought a bus ticket to Miami. I packed two pieces of handbags. I put on a brown sweater and set off to the bus station. After a crazy sixty-four hours on the bus, I arrived in sunny Miami. The drive had completely destroyed my body. I'd rather go to the shopping mall by taxi – I did not want to be late. Inside a luxury department store, I told the guard that I had a scheduled meeting here. He asked for my name, then went to the office. Everywhere around me I saw luxury goods. I quickly checked what handbags are being sold by other luxury companies. I had nothing to worry about. My handbags looked much nicer and they cost much less than theirs. After a while, the pretty lady came to me. Her white crocodile leather boots perfectly matched her long, tanned legs.

You're Mr. Tom Seed, aren't you?

Yes, that's me. Thank you for finding the time for me. I really appreciate it.

You are welcome … please tell me something about yourself, Mr. Seed, In the meantime I'll look at your handbags …

You *probably do not know how it works in this business, Mr. Seed …*

People don't buy expensive things because they have a lot of money to spend on something.

People buy expensive things because of the brand and its status, prestige.

Your handbags look nice, but having nice things is not enough.

There is a reason why you did not sell any handbags.

You are an unknown. No one knows you.

You do not mean anything in this business.

I am sorry.

I'm not interested in working with you …

The most painful words I'd ever heard …

My phone was continually ringing in Los Angeles. I did not pick it up. I received a lot of emails. But I did not answer them. I knew who it was.

I promised something I could not follow through with.

While I was in the motel, someone was waiting for me at the restaurant. I did not dare show my face at an interview with the world's most famous women's magazine journalist. I had ruined my reputation with a journalist from the most famous women's magazine in the world.

For the next three months, I was still waiting for the first order. Then I had to face the facts. I failed.

I had to close my business.

I had spent all my money.

I lost almost three years of my life.

Three years of my life I lost for nothing.

The people around me were never wrong. They were right. I'm just an ordinary loser. I'm twenty-two, and I've never been able to do anything. I never had a girlfriend. I never drove a car.

I've never been on a trip. My whole life was shit. Just like my parents and my grandparents, I will also die in poverty. How could I be so stupid …

How could I think I would be successful?

The entrepreneurial stories that had motivated me had destroyed me now.

Fifteen, sixteen-year-old guys are building multi-million companies, and me?

I'm not able to sell a single fucking handbag.

I've never been able to do anything …

I had to listen to them…

I should have listened to them …

I regretted buying all those "wise" books.

I regretted that I did not enjoy the best years of my youth. If I bought a car and designer clothes with my money, I would not look like I did right now. Like a loser. Without any work. No income. No vision of a more beautiful tomorrow. Only a few dollars, enough to pay for the motel. I was embarrassed to call my former boss. The "stinky" boss. To ask him for a job. He was pleased that I had decided to come back, I regretted the decision to leave. I got the night shift like before. Nothing at all had changed during that period. Except one thing. Yuri went into the retirement he dreamed of so much. Those who knew me looked at me like I had betrayed them. I told them about my millionaire plans, that I would like to be my own boss, while they would be working hard like slaves. Obviously, it did not work out. Now I am the one to laugh at...

Business failure changed me. It changed me a lot. Physically and psychically.

I was no longer the Tom who was working and having fun with his colleagues. The Tom who was enjoying the wind in the back of the dump truck. The Tom who was doing this dirty job with a smile on his face. Now I was the one who was working with hate in his heart because I had to, otherwise I would be out on the street.

Tom, who does not speak with his colleagues because he has no reason to do so.

Tom, who walks with his head bowed down because he feels ashamed about his job... I did hate this job. I did hate these people.

For the last time, I had to work at least twelve hours over the weekend myself because my colleague came to work so drunk he could not stand on his own two feet. I had to do both sides. His left side and my right side, while he was sleeping carelessly drunk in the car. Not only on Saturday, but also on Sunday. Two days in a row! I had an incredible urge to hit him on the head.

I could not bear it anymore. I called the "stinky" boss and told him I was going to resign again. He thought I was a fool because I was about to resign for the second time. He clearly showed me his opinion.

Thirty days. Until then, I had to find a new job.

I promised myself that I would never do dirty work anymore. Never ever. I sent a lot of job applications out.

Salesman, manager, lifeguard, caretaker... when people looked at my CV, I was immediately out of the running. They gave me no chance. For them I was just a nobody without any education. My request had only one purpose. To be thrown away. My inner voice spoke to me, telling me to let it all go. You are not good enough for a decent job. Don't try to be someone else, you are just an ordinary loser. Fortunately, my anger, my desire had defeated my doubts. I began to think completely differently.

You know what?

Maybe I have no education, prestigious work experience, or recommendations from great names, but I have something else.

Something they do not teach at school. I have real life experience. I graduated from the school of life. All those struggles, sacrifices, tears, pain, loss, and trouble gave me something. Difficult times had taught me something. My walls are not decorated with framed diplomas or shiny trophies. The scars are my memories.

Together with my biography, I also sent a letter of motivation, in which I described how I got from the streets off New York to Los Angeles. How I found my previous jobs. I believed it would help. I could do anything. It still took too long to get responses to my job applications. Mostly, when I heard back, they just told me I was not a suitable candidate.

I remembered the time I lived on the street and needed money for food. I remembered very well the way I solved it. I could start drawing again, but I did not have the courage to try it again. I did not risk another failure. Now I needed to find a job with regular income. I can draw in my spare time. I used the advice that Double M had told me.

I opened my eyes and watched closely. Just like that, I did not find anything at that moment. Until late one night, when I was navigating Wilshire Boulevard, I noticed an opportunity. A big billboard advertising a new recording studio. It was opening next week. I immediately put it into my smartphone. After my night shift I went straight to the recording studio from the billboard. I think it could have been 7 am when I got there. A large white truck was parked near the studio. They looked like they were unloading a new device. Only one guy was unloading it himself. He was dressed in a white shirt and I thought he must be the owner. I approached him to ask if he could spare a few minutes of his precious time.

Okay, boy, he answered me. *But first you gotta help me unload these boxes.*

With my bag on my back, I went to work. I did only not help him with those big boxes. Together, we unloaded the entire truck. It took us half a day. Inside the studio, we put each device in its place. Tables, Chairs, Counter, Microphones, Loudspeakers. Real hard work.

Thank you, boy, without you I couldn't have done it myself. How can I repay you?

You know, I'd like to work in your studio, sir.

This is not my studio. I'm the manager. Did you send us your CV? I do not remember seeing you in an interview.

No, sir, I did not send you my CV because I knew where it would end up. With all respect, sir, I came here straight from my night shift. Tired, smelly, dirty. Despite this, I helped you. Half a day I've been carrying heavy boxes out of the truck. I did not stop once. I did not complain once. I did not take a break. I just ask you for one thing. The chance to work for you, sir.

Give me a minute please, I have to make a call.

By his facial expression, I assumed he was offering me a friendly denial. He made the call, pulled up his sleeves on his shirt and looked straight into my eyes. And he said to me:

Your work ethic has made an impression on me. Yesterday we interviewed twenty-five candidates. Each of them sent us a resume. Today we'll choose one of them to be a receptionist. I will tell you honestly that I like you the most. You have courage, which is rare today. Very rare. That's why I am willing to make an exception. Are you sure you can handle such hard work, boy?

Yes sir. I'm sure.

Alright. Tomorrow morning, you start at 8. Be on time.

So I have a job?

Yes, boy. You have a job.

I was thinking: look at yourself! You just won over twenty-five people who had officially asked for this job! The fact that I got this job has to mean something.

You have something they do not have. Boy, believe in yourself! You are better than you think!

It had taken me eleven days to find a new job. I was so excited about it. I was only worried that over the next nineteen days, that I would have to work two different jobs. In the night at that stinky job, during the day as a receptionist at the recording studio.

The first day of the new job I managed admirably, as the manager said. I learned new things. I met new people and I felt especially happy. It was up to me just to survive the last days atmy old job. The other job had taken its toll on me. I was missing my sleep. A lot of sleep. Under my eyes I had dark circles like monocles.

I was physically handling it, but I was overwhelmed by the mental aspects. It depressed me to have to do a job that I did not like at all. I could not wait for the day when I was going to throw dirt into the truck for the last time. I was working twenty hours a day. I looked like a robot.

In the end, this was my choice. I was the one to be blamed for it.

The last night shift in this dirty work. I did not say anything to my colleagues.

In silence, I left the cloakroom with confidence that I would never come back again. The times of self-destruction had ended. The times of dirty work had come to an end. I had reached what I had promised myself. I had taken a massive step forward in my life.

In the studio, my career seemed promising. Me and the manager were among the biggest authorities there. Everyone did what we told to them. Even though I only worked as a receptionist, I was happy with all the success of studio. Musicians fell in love with this place. We were always busy. Over the weekend I went to a night club where the DJs and hip-hop stars knew each other, and me too. They greeted me. They invited me to join in the fun. Girls, young, good-looking girls, sent me Facebook friend requests. After work, we were barbecuing together with my colleagues. I bought a pass for the gym. I passed my driver's license test. I started to save some money to buy a car. I found accommodation in a better neighborhood. Sometimes I even invited a girl on a date, something that would not be considered normal just a few months before. The job switch helped me. It enriched me. In every sphere of mylife. My confidence grew higher and higher.

I enjoyed my work. I was happy to come to the studio, and I was leaving the studio happy, too.

I do not know why, but the job stopped fulfilling me after a while. I felt that emptiness somewhere inside me. I was doing my job out of the habit. Automatically. Not out of passion, like before.

I think I started to feel it when I looked at other people my age posting pictures on Instagram.

They were traveling around the world.

They were visiting all these exotic places, and me?

I was doing the same work every day, at the same time, in the same place. Stuck between four walls in a dark room. I seemed to be a prisoner who was watching the surrounding world through a small window, and within his head he fights questions he does not know the answer.

Is that all?

If this is life, how will I live for the rest of my life?

What if I were out there and not between these walls?

What kind of life would I live instead?

What would I achieve there?

What would I leave behind?

I asked the manager whether he could give me a new role that would take me outside of the studio, in the hope that changing the environment will help me regain the passion, the enthusiasm that I had lost. He accommodated my requests.

I started to drive my clients to and from the studio in a Cadillac Escalade. It really helped me. Changing the environment helped me. I got used to driving around the beautiful streets of Los Angeles. I competed with myself. Each time I tracked how long it took me to take the client from where I picked him up to the studio and back, then and I tried to beat that time. How to take the client faster one way compared to the other. A few minutes back, the client called me telling me where to pick him up. A few minutes later I was waiting in front of his door. All the clients opened the door with the same surprised expression: h*ow did you get here so fast, what the hell*?

The quick rides excited me. The adrenaline in my veins flowed together with the blood. Loud music, hand out of the window, pocket money, world-wide stars in the backseat. No worries. No walls. Freedom on wheels. I could choose the direction to go. I could choose the speed to go. Rihanna, G-Eazy, Post Malone, Chris Brown, Sean 'Diddy' Combs, the musicians I had been listening to on YouTube in the past, they were now in the backseat of my car.

Famous musicians, unknown musicians. Everyone treated me with respect and honor. Whenever I wanted to take a selfie with them, they were willing to take a shot with me. They posed. If one of my friends needed tickets to see Selena Gomez, feel free to call me. I had already sold VIP tickets on eBay for a very good price. Even though all those stars spend thousands of dollars on clothes, watches, jewelry, holidays and cars, they are still human beings with kind hearts, full of emotion and respect. I knew people who were willing to give me a nice load of money just to have an hour of my job.

One day when I was taking Seal to the studio. I asked him how he managed to get out of misery to reach the heights of stardom.

I believed in myself more than the people in my neighborhood believed in themselves.

This was his answer.

A few weeks later I brought him again to the studio. This time he asked me the question: *what is your mission?* I thought long and hard about it, but I did not know the answer.

Don't worry about it, he told me. *It will take years to find out what our missions are. In most cases, we find our mission only when we fall to the bottom. Then we begin to think about ourselves, our lives and the real reasons for who we are, what we want and why we are here.*

A few months later, minor problems started popping up in the studio. The guy who replaced me as the receptionist was really sick and I had to go back between those four walls again. Surprisingly, I did not mind. I felt like I was there for the first time. Maybe because I had more time to think, concentrating on myself, I again started to feel the same feelings of emptiness as before.

It was as if one part of me wanted to be here, while the other part had a desire to be somewhere else.

What if it's time to change the job? I asked myself.

I had gained a lot of experience. It shouldn't be hard to find a new job. I tried to wait a few days, but my feelings did not change. There was no medicine for my diagnosis. So I took a deep breath and went to the manager's office. Instead of the manager, there was a tall guy I'd never seen before.

Hello *Tom, glad to meet you. I'm John, the owner of this recording studio.*

This is the owner? I thought. He was wearing a t-shirt and shorts.

I've heard a lot about you, Tom. I'm honored that a talented man like you works for me.

What do you mean, John?

Don't be so modest. I saw your portrait drawing, which you donated to Mike and his friend Bill and Double M.

How do you know them? I was so surprised that I had to ask him.

I was his roommate back while he was in college. Even though he spent most of the time studying something, we were never bored when we were together. We stayed in touch since those days. Well, when they diagnosed him with cancer, I offered him help. I insisted on it. But he refused it. He chose a free life on the streets.

That's where I had met them, John, on the street...

Over the weekend, all three of them worked for me. They looked after my house. They were mowing the lawn, watering the flowers, washing my cars.

Not for money. For food.

A few days before it happened, we were grilling some steaks at my home out in the backyard. That day they told me about you, that you are a very brave and smart young man who had to come out to California from New York. They also showed me the portrait you drew. The portrait they still kept with them like a good luck charm. They missed you, Tom. They were waiting for you on the street where you met them the first time. They wanted to be with you. To listen to stories about your success, your failures. For them, you were like their own son. You meant a lot to them. So much.

When I listened to his words, tears started streaming down my face.

Tell me, Tom, how do you like your job here? Do you feel good about this job?

The truth was I used to like it. Now it's different. I came here to tell you I'm going to probably resign.

What led you to this decision? Is there anything I can do for you?

You know from the beginning I loved this work. It made me feel great. But now I feel emptiness when I'm here. I'm bored here. Time passes very slow here. I think a new job will change this.

What kind of work do you mean?

I don't know yet. Maybe a taxi driver or courier.

I'm not so worried about it. I found this job in eleven days. I will find something later as well.

A taxi driver? You're kidding me. You are a natural artist. This is the direction you must take. You've discovered your talent. Now you just must do something with it.

Don't waste your talent. Ninety-nine percent of the people in this world are wasting their talents. Do not be like them.

It's not as easy as you think. I come from a poor family. My parents worked like regular blue-collar workers. Their parents worked as regular blue-collar workers. They were born in poverty. They died in poverty. Nobody in my family has never been able to achieve anything. Nobody!

And? Is this your justification? You do not have to live the same life that your parents or grandparents lived. Tom, you have the power to change it. You have the skills and talent that your parents did not have. So use it to your advantage! Don't let other people determine your future, your life.

I'm not sure about my success with drawing. I tried to start a business and I failed. I don't want to experience it again. I'd rather work for someone else, where I'm sure to have a regular monthly income.

You surprise me, Tom. At such a young age, you've done more than other people could do in a lifetime. Tell me what did you do?

Fashion. I designed my own handbags and

I had them handmade in Italy. I wanted to sell them to rich women here. But I did not sell a single piece. I lost all my money.

Interesting. Why do you think you failed, Tom, as an entrepreneur?

You know John, nobody wanted to buy those handbags. I read many books and articles, like other entrepreneurs who succeeded, and did exactly what they did. With no results. I believed so much that I had the ability to prove it. I put all my energy, effort, time, money into it. I did everything, and yet I failed. I could not do anything about it. I replied with great disappointment in my voice.

You are wrong, Tom. This is not the reason why you have failed as an entrepreneur.

What do you mean?

Why did you decide to start a business? What made you start a business?

I had to think about the real reason why I started doing business. Then I told him: I was listening to a lot of conversations, reading a lot of books that made me believe that a business was the best way to make $ 1 million, so I could do what I like for the rest of my life.

Like drawing, am I right?

Yes, you are right. If I was a wealthy entrepreneur, without having to worry about paying for meals or rent, I could draw peacefully for the rest of my life.

So, the real reason why you started doing business was that you heard, or you read about some people who made millions of dollars by starting the right business. Correct?

Yes exactly.

Mmm. Now listen to me very carefully.

Some can find success as an entrepreneur, but it does not mean you can get the same, Tom! You failed because you put all your energy, effort, time and money into the wrong place. Your business required an extraordinary salesperson with a wealth of experience, but you are not an extraordinary salesperson, Tom.

You are extraordinary at drawing, not at sales. I know a lot of people, especially young people like you, who started doing business because they wanted to be like Bill Gates, Mark Zuckerberg, Elon Musk, or Mark Cuban. And do you think they have succeeded? No! Of course they failed! They failed. They failed like you.

Because they did not have the skills, talent, personality, experience, dreams, and vision like Bill Gates, Mark Zuckerberg, Elon Musk, or Mark Cuban.

It's like when a short person chooses to be the world's top basketball player just because he recently read an article in a magazine that basketball players date the most beautiful women.

Every day, he trains as hard as LeBron James.

He practices the same exercises as LeBron James.

He uses the same nutritional supplements as LeBron James. But he will never become a basketball player like LeBron James. He just was not made for basketball.

Wait, John. You can't compare sports and business. They are totally different.

Why, Tom? What's so different about them?

They are the same! Just look around. There are two groups of people. Extraordinary people and ordinary people. Those who are extraordinary live an extraordinary life and achieve extraordinary results because they find what they are extraordinary in and do what they are extraordinary in. And those who are ordinary live ordinary lives and achieve ordinary achievements because they find what they are ordinary in and do what they are ordinary in.

That's why they are where they are. Extraordinary people use their strengths, while ordinary people use their weaknesses. That's all there is to it. Choose and focus on one of them. Every person in this world has his or her own choice. If you want to belong to the group of extraordinary people, Tom, you must do what's extraordinary for you, put everything into it and success will come.

Maybe not tomorrow.

Maybe not next month.

Maybe not next year.

Maybe not for three years, but if you endure, I guarantee that your life will not be the same as before.

Why do most people choose their weaknesses instead of their strengths?

Because they deceive. They deceive themselves.

They do not see reality. Instead of sacrificing one day of their life thinking about themselves, where they could sincerely admit who they really are, what their strengths and weaknesses are, so they could choose the right direction. The direction that would lead them to the top.

Instead of doing what are they extraordinary in, they do something completely different, useless, for their whole life. And then they are wailing, crying, wondering why they've lost everything in their lives.

Why are they still down. Why they are not successful. Why are they unhappy.

They try to be someone they are not. Like the tiny basketball player.

There are, of course, a few exceptions that have found what they are extraordinary in, but still remain in the shadow of being ordinary. They remain in the shadow of being ordinary because they did not believe in themselves –that they are able to achieve excellence.

A lack of self-confidence, fear, the opinions of others overtook their talents and abilities.

By the way, if you think millions of dollars in your bank account gives you the freedom to do the things you do and like, you are wrong. Money has nothing to do with it. It's all about you. The opinions of other people have forced you to believe that only if you have millions in your bank account can you do what you love for the rest of your life, but the truth is that by doing just what you love, you can have millions in your bank account for the rest of your life.

How did you reach your success, John? To trust his advice, I had to ask him. I needed proof.

I was waiting for you to ask this question. I was born, and I grew up in Czechoslovakia, where communists were still in power. It's a whole different life than America. My parents owned a small chicken farm in the countryside. Such a small village in a forest of less than a thousand people. I started working with my parents since my sixth birthday. I fed the chickens, cleaned them, and I also collected eggs, which I then carried on my mom's bicycle to the surrounding villages where I sold them at the markets. I'll tell you that it took me more than an hour to get from our farm to the nearest village. In the rain. In the snow. In storms. I always took my mom's purple bike. Every day I got up very early. Earlier than my parents, just to be able to be at the market for as long as possible. In the dark I left the house, and I returned home after dark. I really loved it. Of course I had days when I hated it. But it only happened to me when some cruel person punctured my bicycle tires and I had to go for almost three hours alongside the bicycle on foot. I still do not know who destroyed those wheels to this day.

Meanwhile, as I walked back from market, I spoke to people. To many people. When I stood in the market with a willow basket in my hand, people walked up to me only for one purpose alone. To buy chicken eggs. But thanks to my passion for conversation, they took home more than just the chicken eggs. They took an experience. Already at such a young age, I was able to engage, warm up and excite people. It did not take long before they started to talk about me in the surrounding villages, about the show I was putting on at the markets. One day, a visitor came from a remote town to our farm. The director of the Primary Art School. He came to ask for permission from my parents. He wanted me to attend his primary school, where I would be part of the theater course. Fortunately, my parents agreed. Visiting that school brought such huge changes to my life. I had to travel sixteen miles a day on such an old bus, there and back. The time I spent selling chicken eggs at the market was cut very short. At school I was one of the ordinary students, but in the school's theater I was an extraordinary actor. I was a star on the stage.

Our theater won all the district competitions. In addition to performing on stage, I had one more hobby. Recording my voice on the recorder. I took my father's sports newspaper, hid myself with the chickens in shed, and there I read the sports articles. I save all those recordings from the newspapers. In some of them, you can even hear the sound of the chickens in the background...

I know it's funny to you, but trust me! Life in that country looked completely different than life here in America. Almost every family was home to pigs, ducks or goats. When we wanted to drink milk, we had to milk our cows. They asked for crazy amounts of money in the shops for milk. We gathered the water in a metal bucket from the well. We only had one toilet. A wooden toilet outdoors in the garden ...

Why did you record your voice in the shed with the chickens, John?

You know Tom, my parents had other ideas about what I should do in my free time. The only place where I found some peace, where I would not have to hear the restrictive speech of my parents, was in the shed with the chickens. Only there I could do what I loved. Those chickens did not judge me like my parents did. My parents did not support me because I did not help them with the farm. They minded that that I spent my time by myself, not with them and their farm.

I had devoted myself to these two hobbies by the time I turned nineteen. After graduating from secondary school, I chose a different way.

I was looking after inner myself.

What kind of work I could do.

My first job was to drive a tractor on a local farm. I stayed there for four months. That's how my enthusiasm for driving disappeared so quickly.

I found my second job in the city where I worked as a mailman. On a bicycle I delivered packages and checks. Again, from the beginning, I enjoyed it, but after a while it stopped being so interesting for me. My excitement disappeared. So after one year, I quit.

In my third job I worked as railroad conductor. This was my longest job. Eighteen months. Then I fell into a serious depression. I did not know what to do. I did not enjoy anything. Nothing brought a smile to my face. I was unemployed. I hated it when I had to meet some of my friends my age. I hated it because while they talked about their perfect lives, I was thinking about my terrible life. After ten months of no work I said enough! Enough.

At twenty, I decided to change my life. I stopped thinking short term, I stopped thinking only about money. Instead I started to think long term. What am I supposed to do that I would be willing to do the rest of my life for free?

When does time go by so fast?

When do I feel the happiest?

I remember that day very well when I realized it. It was Saturday night. I sat outside in the garden watching the stars in the sky and cried. I cried because I knew what I wanted to do, but I was afraid to do it. I was afraid I would not be good at it. I was afraid what other people would think of me. It took me three weeks before I decided to do it. I left the comfort of my parent's house and moved to the city. I started working on the radio as a traffic moderator. The money I earned was enough for accommodation and my meals.

At that time, people around me looked at me like I was a loser.

I had nothing …

No girlfriend.

No car.

No house.

No experiences.

While they had everything …

A well-paid job.

Their own car.

Their own house.

A beautiful girlfriend.

Vacations.

The truth is that it did bother me at first. I was jealous. I wanted to live the life they lived. But then I realized that I was different. I had other goals, plans, dreams. I did not need what they have. I focused on my talent, what made me happy. Not on my bank account.

For the first time in my life, I started to work for pleasure, not for money.

Since I started working on the radio, my life became perfect. My body was full of incredible energy. I had such a positive energy in myself. I felt fantastic.

One year later, I became the moderator of my own show. I interviewed the most successful people in our country. Politicians, athletes, entrepreneurs. The guests listening to my show admired me. Almost every day someone told me: you have a gift for speaking. You have a gift of words. Your voice is so beautiful. It all fit together.

In my childhood, I shone as a shopkeeper at the market. In my adulthood I was a shining star as a radio moderator.

I succeeded because I'm an extraordinary speaker.

I received the art of speech as gift from God. My greatest honor was providing the commentary for the Summer Olympics in 1996. Everyone in the country knew my voice. In less than two years, I took such huge steps from being a traffic moderator to having my own show. I earned more in one month than my friends earned in six months.

I bought my first car.

I rented a small apartment on the outskirts of the city. Nothing more!

I did not spend my hard-earned money on luxuries.

A few years later I was given the opportunity to dub movies. I took this opportunity. From the radio I moved to the recording studio. I spent the whole day in the studio. I did not need to do things like the other people in my age. The studio gave some meaning to my life.

How did you make it from a recording studio in Czechoslovakia to Los Angeles? I asked him excitedly.

In 1999 I visited the Los Angeles International Film Festival. This was the first time I ever visited the United States. I fell in love with it so much that I decided to move here. To live my American Dream. But it did not work without any issues of course. Getting a green card in that period for people like me was almost impossible. Without it, I could not live here legally. For me, there was only one option to live legally in America. To create my own company that employed American citizens.

It took me three years before I earned the money to start my dream. I sold my car, I packed some clothes in my suitcase and left for Los Angeles.

I came here sixteen years ago. When I got here, I opened my own recording studio. I'll tell you Tom, my beginnings were hard. Very hard. I did not know English well. I did not know anyone, and nobody knew me. I was sleeping in my studio on a mattress. I could not afford to pay rent.

I had a studio.

I had employees.

But I did not have any clients.

No profit.

I personally visited every singer, every movie studio in this town. I offered them the opportunity to record in my studio almost free of charge. Because of my weak English, I could not do it over the phone. But the fact that I made the effort to tell them personally, face to face, impressed them. They accepted my offer. I got my first clients. I turned my disadvantage into my advantage. I preferred personal contact, and my clients preferred personal contact.

It was exactly eleven months before I could afford to stay outside of my studio. Then I met Mike. His parents owned an apartment in Montecito Heights, where he had been living. He had one room there. That room became my second home. It would never happen if Mike did not come to my studio to record a speech for an event in school. While Mike spent time at school, or studying in the library, I was working.

Every day I traveled by bus around California and approached musicians. Both large and small names. Known and unknown. It took me months to reach out to every musician in California. I had to sacrifice a lot of things to afford it.

I wore the same clothes that I came with.

I ate only two meals a day.

I washed dirty clothes on the side, so Mike could give me a discount for my room.

Even though the studio earned some money, I did not even take a penny from it. I lived off the money

I earned by working in my homeland. And I tell you, it was not much.

At that time, only three recording studios were

Located in Los Angeles. One of them was owned by me. When the news about my studio spread to the musicians, I started receiving a lot of requests to book the studio. Musicians who had previously recorded their songs at my competition were coming to me. The few musicians who recorded with me told other musicians about my approach. As long as my competitors did it for the money, I did it for pleasure. It brought them to me. I did not have to convince them. They came by themselves. And these musicians introduced me to the woman who has been my wife for more than ten years.

In addition to a better price, my studio gave them something else. The feeling of home. I took care of my clients more than my clients' money. Every musician who recorded in my studio knows me personally. My wife and I still send them fruit baskets nowadays, as a thank you.

The best thing about it is that even if I do not do it for the money, I earn more than the other studios in this country.

I am forty-five years old, owning six recording studios, and earning millions of dollars doing what I love. And my friends from school who laughed at me in the past? They are now at work doing something they hate, because they bought large toys in their youth with money they did not have.

It all started with my decision. To do what I'm extraordinary at. To talk.

I have succeeded because in addition to hard work, I used my strengths, not my weaknesses. This is the path you have to go as well, Tom! Focus on just one thing.

Drawing.

That's your strong suit.

That's what makes you special.

That's what you were born to do.

Now it all made sense to me. I already understood why a framed photograph was hanging on the wall with the guys behind the table holding a microphone in their hands. He's that sports commentator. In his youth he looked different, so different that I did not even recognize him.

John, I got to tell you something. From the start I did not believe what you said. I had doubts. I'd like to apologize to you. I was wrong about you. I really admire you. You did a remarkable thing.

That's alright. Don't worry. It happens to me very often. People think that only those who wear tailored suits and gold watches must be successful. I do not need to make any impression of having expensive things on anyone. I do not need to prove anything to anyone. I'm still modest, even though I have a lot of money. I know the value of money very well. Trust me. Nobody ever gave me anything in my life for free. Everything that I now have, I've gotten with my own hands.

The more I listened to him, the more I realized how stupid I was. John, I want to do something with myself as well! With my life! I want to be someone. Somebody like you. But I do not know how! What should I do?

For the rest of my life, do I have to stand on the street next to a wooden stand, drawing the people passing by for a few dollars? I barely earn enough money for rent drawing on the street.

There is no doubt that you have talent. Great talent. Unfortunately, your fears are killing it. Your talent is like a seed hiding in its shell. The shell is your fear. Fear, the lack of courage to take risks, keeps you where you are now. You are afraid!

What if I fail?

What if I succeed?

You lost long before you tried to win. Instead of risk, you chose to be sure. Regular work on behalf of the dreams of other people in the hope that once you have enough money, you will start doing what you are extraordinary at, what you love.

The sad thing is that this will never happen. Tom, one day you will die. Your talent, your abilities, your potential, your dreams, they will all die with you. Unopened, unfulfilled, unused. Just remember Double M and what he did. He waited too long. Do not be afraid of failure, Tom. It's part of success. Be grateful.

Thanks to your failure as an entrepreneur, you found out what you are ordinary at. Now you are wiser, more experienced. Now you can do what are you extraordinary at for the rest of your life.

Break that shell, Tom! Get rid of your limitations. You can work on other people's dreams any time. Work will always be here after our death. But the time we have to fulfill our potential is limited. So start working on yourself, for yourself. Do not waste your talents. Work on it. Develop it. Use it.

So, in your opinion, John, I should stop working for other people?

Yes, Tom! Definitely! Every time you feel emptiness. The problem is not at work. The problem is in you. Deep inside you, you know you should draw. This is a blank space that needs to be filled. Drawing fills the emptiness.

Why did no one ever tell me this?

Why didn't I read it in those books? I have at least forty books on the shelf and I never read this.

You searched in the wrong place. On the Internet, in books. In the outside world. But, all you need to find is inside you. In your inner world. Only there you will find what you are looking for.

Of course books are useful. I also read them. However, reading books alone is not enough. Millions of people around the world read books that give them advice, tips on how to get rich, how to be happy and win friends, how to lose weight, how to be a great parent. Whatever your goal is, you will always find a book about it. The truth is that of those millions of people reading, only a handful of them achieve success in any area of life.

You know why? Because while they read, someone else is working. Hard work outside your comfort zone will always beat being comfortable in a soft bed with a book in hand. So far, you have read books on how to build a million-dollar company. From now on, I recommend reading books how to build a millionaire's mindset.

Read them only when you can stand in front of a mirror with your head up to say honestly to yourself: Today I have done all the necessary, difficult, important, unpleasant things that will bring me tomorrow closer to my goal, to my dream, to my success. If you cannot do it in every day of your life, I guarantee that no book will help you. Got it?

Yes, I got it.

Do not rely on books. Trust yourself!

Where should I start, John?

Where you ended. On the street.

Really?

On the street?

Yes, on the street.

It is not important where you start, what is important is just to get started. Today you can draw here on the dirty streets of Los Angeles, and tomorrow you could be drawing in the White House. I also started out surrounded by those chickens.

Steve Jobs also started in the garage. Michael Phelps also started in a backyard garden pool. Beyoncé also started singing in her school's choir. So you do not need to start in a five-star luxury apartment. Just start. Everything else happens afterwards.

What if no one is interested in my drawings? There were many people at the beach, but only a few were willing to buy them.

Do not look at the tree when the forest is here. Dream big dreams. With your talent you can be an architect, a fashion designer, a product designer …

Anything you can believe you can be. Everything is about your mindset. You will get what you ask for.

Actually, I'm sure I would be an extraordinary architect. I was always fascinated with buildings.

The problem is I do not have a high school education, John. I do not think I have the chance to become an architect without an education.

The problem would be, Tom, if you have to work for someone else, but you can work for yourself. You do not need to have a degree or a diploma. Among the most successful and richest people in the world are not just those who have university degrees. Not at all.

There are mostly people without higher education, without even a high school education.

Do you know Eminem or Richard Branson?

Of course, John, I know both of them.

So if they can do it, you can do it! Trust me.

But how?

How do I get from portrait drawings to drawing buildings?

Just like me. Sometimes I gained experience with someone else. Who gathered it all of their life. I learned how to work out how to breathe properly, how to articulate, how to work with the microphone, how to use the recording software. I learned everything I needed to become an extraordinary speaker. When I learned all this, I set out on my own way. I opened my own recording studio.

I don't understand, John, you just recommended not to work for someone else and now you recommend the opposite?

Good question, Tom. Let me explain it to you. If you want to be the best, you have to learn from the best. Even at the cost of working for someone else. But in this case, you are not working on other people's dreams. You are working on your own dreams. Within a few months, you can learn what someone else has spent decades acquiring. You could take an internship in an architectural firm where you would gain the necessary experience to open your own architectural studio. If I'm right, you've worked for about five years for someone else.

Yes, John, you are right.

So why should it be a problem for you to spend six months on an internship, so that you can do what you love for the rest of your life. To draw.

It's only six months. Six months that will change your whole life. You must be patient. No shortcuts. Forget your past, you cannot change it. Right now, you have the opportunity to change your future. So do it.

Just look at yourself, Tom! You did a job in which you did not use your talents, your abilities, and yet you were one of the best. Just like in my studio. And now imagine what you would be able to achieve at the job you were born for. Unbelievable things. Unbelievable things.

I felt such a strong desire, such a strong motivation to actually do it. Achieve something.

You're right, John, I totally agree with you.

This is the direction I have to follow.

This is the direction I am determined to channel my motivation.

I was impressed.

Another boss would have asked me to stay.

Perhaps I would have been offered a higher salary, premiums, or paid vacation. My boss, John, asked me to leave. So that I would not waste my talent.

We agreed that if I received an internship for thirty days, I would continue to work in the studio but only part-time. Thanks to this I would have enough time to develop my talent. In my case, this meant washing floors in the afternoon and driving clients from studio or to the studio over the weekends.

I liked the idea of making decent money by drawing. John had opened my eyes. I just needed to push myself in the right direction. Now all this was left to me and nobody else. To take the first step.

In Los Angeles, I wrote eleven architectural companies with an internship application. My request was rejected by almost all of them. Except for two companies.

One of them I had to reject. The training was about to start in two months, which was too late for me. I had, made an agreement with John. I've reviewed the second business on the Internet. Their projects looked good. The reviews from former employees sounded good. The list of their clients was admirable. I decided to risk it. An internship at this company would start in six days. I got an invitation to participate in an e-mail.

And I accepted it.

I was a bit disappointed that they wanted to choose only one person. Then I remembered how I got this job at John's studio, which calmed me down.

At John's recommendation, I took the day off and went back to where I started. On the street.

I put my big wooden stand covered with a thick layer of dust back in my old happy place. Since the last time I had been there, nothing had changed. There was the same ice cream guy with his stall. The seagulls in the sky made the same crazy sounds. Only one thing had changed. My mission. To draw for joy, not for money.

Some people recognized me from before. They did not hide their enthusiasm that I had come back. This time I did not try to sell my drawings to people. I really wanted to get acquainted with them. Who they are, what they do, what their view on my drawings is. Without hesitation they shared with me their life stories. It looked like an exhibition by a well-known artist. I enjoyed it very much. I was interested in other people and they were interested in me.

And my feeling of emptiness?

I no longer felt it anymore. It had disappeared.

Now I was happy.

Really happy.

A smile on my face.

A twinkle in my eyes.

Peace of mind.

This is what I really loved.

This is why I was born.

Today was my day. The big day. My internship interview would begin in less than two hours. I tried not to stress. Be calm, relaxed.

I closed my eyes and imagined what it would be like when I was successful at my internship. I assured myself that I would do it. Still, I have managed much more challenging things. When I arrived at the headquarters of an architectural firm, no one except me was there. I was first to arrive and still had a lot of time left. Just be sure I was punctual. Meanwhile, as I was waiting, I admired the photos of all the buildings designed by the company.

I saw myself walking here every day and working on big projects. I was expecting only success that day. Nothing else.

As I was waiting for my great moment, the other applicants for the internship started arriving as well. I sat down in the chair and looked busy. Like I was doing something important on my smartphone. In fact, I was not doing anything with it, just looking at the screen and touching my fingers to open and close the apps. I did not want to look strange. Everyone in the room was doing something on their smartphone. Everyone …

The silence was interrupted the secretary's soft voice announcing the opening of the interviews. There was tension in the room. We were all nervously waiting until they called our name. Time was ticking slower, and my heart was beating faster. I'd rather hide my smartphone in my bag, because if I did not do that, it would slip from my hands to the ground. My palms were that sweaty.

I looked around curiously. At my rivals. I looked at them very carefully. Each one was dressed in a fancy suit. Polished shoes. In their hands they kept a book with portfolios of their work. I did not care about them. But the longer I waited, the more I stopped believing in myself. I started to doubt myself.

Look at these guys! They're wearing expensive suits, they have so much experience … they have a fancy diploma from prestigious schools … And you?

You're sitting here alone dressed in cheap jeans and in a white shirt. Without any portfolio. No diploma. I wasn't ready. Clearly not today.

I stood up and with my head bowed I started to shamefully make my way out of the room. I did not have the courage to even tell the secretary.

I was talking to myself the whole time:

I'm going to be better in the future.

I will prepare better in the future.

Next time I will do it.

Next time I will do it.

I was angry with myself. I had to be better prepared. For a while, I stopped at the jewelry store. I did not stay there because I wanted to look at the gold rings. I stood there because I saw myself in the reflection like I was looking in the mirror. I was looking at that weak person in my body. I could not stand to look anymore.

Is that all you can do?!

After all the sacrifices, the difficulties, the failures?

I started crying. I started crying because I knew I would not get a second chance. Damn! It was now or never.

I wiped the tears off my face and ran faster than I ever could. I did not want to miss my chance. Through red lights at the traffic lights. Through crowds of people. Workers on the sidewalk. Nothing slowed me down. Nothing could stop me.

I jumped, I avoided, I destroyed all the obstacles standing in my way.

Sweaty and breathless, I sat down on the chair beside the two remaining guys, hoping to get back in time. I did not need an expensive suit. I did not need a fancy portfolio. I did not need a fancy diploma. I can do it without all these things.

Ten minutes later, I heard the kind voice of the secretary calling my name. *Tom Seed, please come in.*

I made it. I made it. Yes!

I entered a huge modern office with a carbon table where two guys were sitting, clearly in a good mood. One of them noticed the sweat on my forehead.

God, man, what, did you run to catch the bus? He remarked enthusiastically.

Something like that, sir. Something similar …

Oh my God, the perfect start. I thought.

I'd like to introduce you to Mr. Moriss. Mr. Moriss is the director of this company, which he founded just seven years ago. Our employees are the key to our success. Therefore, anyone who would like to work here, even only as a trainee, attends an interview with the directors.

Nice to meet you, Mr. Moriss.

I would be honored to work for your business, which is one of the best in the entire United States.

Thank you for the kind words. I really appreciate it. Please tell us, Mr. Seed, what brings you here?

Passion Mr. Moriss. Passion for drawing brings me here. My response made no great impression on him.

When did you find out that you had a talent for drawing?

Even back in my childhood. At school I drew other things like the other kids at my age. While they were drawing circles, or cubes, I drew houses, people, cars, animals. Everything I imagined in my head I put on paper. I drew the slightest details.

Interesting. Why did you decide to become an architect at twenty-three years old when you knew about your talent in drawing at such a young age?

Because I allowed the people, the environment around me, to determine the direction of my life. This is my answer to your question.

Can I look at your portfolio?

I have to be honest Mr. Moriss. I have no portfolio here. All of the drawings I've made are either stored on my nightstand or hanging up on the walls of someone's house in frame.

On the wall?

Yes, on the wall. I recently started drawing again at the beach, like when I was living on the street. I have a wooden stand on which I draw anything people ask me. From a baby in the stroller to the seagulls in the sky. Whatever. I suppose I know what you think of me now, sir. I am not wondering, but if you giv …

Wait! I think I've heard about you somewhere.

I just cannot remember where.

I had no idea what he was talking about.

While he was looking for something on the Internet, I looked over his office with my eyes. Wherever I looked I saw awards. So many awards.

Found it! He shouted. *Look, Joshua, I saw him here. Mr. Seed, do you know that you are very popular? The Los Angeles Times wrote an article about you.*

I felt an unpleasant pain in my stomach. What have I done to make them write about me in the newspaper? I asked myself.

You also have a photo as you're drawing behind your wooden stand, right next to an ice cream stall.

What? I was seeing it for the first time. I did not know about it at all.

Being you, I would frame it and hang it somewhere on the wall. It's remarkable. Very remarkable.

Well, thank you.

Tell us why we should choose you? Mr. Seed.

One guy told me that if you want to be the best, you have to learn from the best. I'm determined to be the best. To be the best architect. That's why I'm here Mr. Moriss.

As you could see, there were thirty-seven candidates today. Thirty-seven highly talented candidates. Only one of you will gain the valuable experience as part of my business for the next six months. If my assistant Joshua calls you tomorrow, that means we have chosen you. If Joshua does not call you tomorrow, we've chosen someone else. Thank you for your participation, Mr. Seed. Have a nice day.

I was struggling with a huge cheeseburger on a bench by the beach when my phone began to give off a strange sound. An incoming call from an unknown number. I jumped with joy. I was literally flying in the clouds.

I did it.

Joshua called me. They had accepted me.

I will be the best architect in Los Angeles. Woo Hoo ... I'll show you world, who I am!

With such an incredibly good mood, I ran over to the studio to tell John this great news. He did not hide enthusiasm. Together we were jumping with joy as one team.

Tell me all the details, Tom. I want to know everything.

You know, John, I have to tell you the truth. In the morning, I woke up with the belief that I was a good candidate for the internship. I believed in myself.

I went there confidently with only one purpose. To land the internship.

When I got there and waited for the other guys to come, I lost my conviction, confidence, my certainty that I was the one who could do it that day. I started to doubt myself. It made me feel weak.

Those guys were better dressed, better prepared than I was. It all meant that one of them would be accepted, not me. So I stood up and walked away like a coward. On the sidewalk I stopped at the shop. I looked at my own reflection in the shop window. I was crying.

Then I remembered something. I wiped my tears from my face and ran back quickly so I wouldn't miss my interview.

I can imagine how you looked after you were running in the hot weather.

It did not seem ridiculous to me at the time, but now we were laughing with each other.

The director of the company asked me a few typical questions. After answering one of them, he told me that he had heard about me somewhere. Imagine this John, they wrote about me in The Los Angeles Times as I was drawing on the beach. I could not believe my own eyes.

I'm sure this impressed the director.

I think the same. Before the interview ended, he told me that if his assistant Joshua calls today, they chose me for an internship. If he did not call me, they accepted someone else. But he called. Joshua called me.

I'm very proud of you, Tom. What made you come back to the interview? What were you thinking about then?

I remembered our friends. Mike, Bill, and Double M. I did not want to have the same thing happen to me as well. They gave me advice.

What advice, Tom? Share it with me.

I felt like I was standing there with them on that dark street. I still had that image in my head. So Mike advised me:

If you want to do something, you have to do it.

No matter how, no matter where, no matter with whom.

I have nothing to put off. And when my inner voice says tomorrow, I have to close my eyes and do it now. Right now. I realized that there would be no next time. So I ran back.

I guess Mike told you about a friend of mine, who was in love with him head over heels, and him too.

Yes, John. He told me about her.

What advice did Bill give you?

Bill told me: I should take full responsibility for my life, my deeds. I should not naively think that someone in this world would take care of me. I do not have to complain, fool around, make excuses, regret and blame others. And when I'm not happy with my life, I have to close my mouth and work for a better life. So I stopped regretting it and went back to the interview for the chance at a better life.

Tom, I cannot wait for the advice that Double M gave you.

Double M told me to be open to anything, to always go for your dreams. I only get to live one life, we only get one chance. And when the people around me scream, I should just cover my ears and carry on. I realized I would not get another chance. So I did not throw it away.

The advice they gave you is valuable. Very valuable. They had a reason why they just gave this to you, Tom. What they learned in their entire life they have summed for you up in a few words.

Very valuable words. Now, in your twenties, you know what they found out in their forties, fifties.

I'm very grateful for it, John. I will never forget them.

You know what was still admirable about Mike, Bill, and Double M?

No, John, I do not know.

They lived on the street like the homeless, didn't they?

Yes, they lived on the street like happy warriors.

Warriors?

Yes, warriors. That's what I call all the homeless people. You know life on the street taught me that, except for winter, hunger, thirst, dirt, poverty, violence, you have to fight with even one more enemy. The greatest enemy. Yourself.

You got that right. The biggest struggles do not happen on the battlefield, but in our minds. This advice, people living on the street have shared it. Modestly dressed, without property, without money, without food. So you cannot judge a book by its cover. The fact that someone is better dressed than you, driving a car better than you, having a better smartphone than you, that he is in a better home than you, he has better job than you, does not mean that he's better than you.

Similarly, the opposite is true. If someone is worse dressed than you, is driving a worse car than you, has a worse smartphone than you, lives in a worse house than you, has worse job than you do, that does not mean he is worse than you are.

This is why you should stop watching TV. This is why you should stop looking at other people's photos on social networks. Because when you see a photo of a man who is enjoying the summer in Ibiza while you are drawing at a table at home, you start comparing yourself with him.

You're home, he's in Ibiza. While you sit at home behind a table alone, he sits behind a bar with five sexy girls. You work, he travels. It forces you to doubt yourself. Forcing you to compare yourselves. Tom, if you really want to be happy, never compare yourself to anyone. Never! Everyone has their own dreams, goals, life values. Everybody is different, everybody wants something different. You understand?

Yes, John, I understand. Now I know why I felt so bad when I looked at the photos of Dan Bilzerian on his Instagram. I'll stop it now.

So I recommend doing that! Over the last days, Tom, you have learned a lot. You did what you wanted. In addition to making good decisions, you made also wrong decisions. This is normal. It is natural to make mistakes. But making the same mistake twice is stupid.

You are a very extraordinary man, Tom. From the very first moment you entered my office, I knew you were born for great things. You know, since I opened my first recording studio, a lot of people have worked for me. Hundreds. You are the first to ask me how I succeeded in achieving my success. Thanks to you, I know that all the achievements I have achieved have been from good reasons.

Seeing how you move forward in life, how you overcome your limitations and use your potential, makes me happy. So happy...Today, Tom, you've proved to me that you're ready.

Ready for what, John?

For my gift. Please open it.

He handed me a brown envelope closed with a red ribbon.

Money?

Tickets to the LA Clippers?

A permanent membership to Gold's Gym?

There was something inside it. I put the ribbon down and carefully opened the mysterious envelope. Inside was a pen and two clean white sheets of paper with my name.

I suppose you expected something else, right?

No! It is perfect. Thank you. I really appreciate it.

Of course, I thought first of all that this kind of a stupid thing as a gift, but then I realized that except for Mike, Bill, Double M, and John, nobody had ever given me anything.

Let me explain why you just got these two things. Every day, something happens in our lives.

Sometimes something good happens to us. Sometimes something bad happens to us. In any case, our habit is to remember just the bad and forget about the good.

All our experiences, knowledge, and thoughts are kept in our minds. Sometimes we have positive ones. Sometimes we keep the negative ones. Again, in any case, our habit is to remember only the negative and to forget about the positive ones.

Now you have to get rid of this habit. Distinguish between the good and bad. The positive from the negative. Get that poisonous weed out of your mind.

This pen represents me, a human being. And these papers should be my mind. Correct?

Exactly. You got it right.

How do I separate the good from bad, positive from negative?

Simple. Take the pen and write down on the first sheet all your negative, constraining opinions, beliefs, thoughts, and memories. Everything poisonous that kills you inside.

On the second sheet, write down all your successes and victories. Everything positive that makes you stronger from the inside.

It takes a lot of time. Concentrate. That's why

I'll leave you here now, I'm going to take my dog Brutus out to the beach. Take your time. Time is your friend, not your enemy.

John stood up and walked away peacefully.

I thought it would be easy to write something on those papers. I underestimated it. I really had to think about myself and my life. I returned to the very beginning. Where it all began. To my childhood.

I analyzed every day of my life. Little by little.

It took hours. Black ink filled the blank space on the paper.

Then I saw it. Back then, in Manhattan, I did not destroy those luxury cars because I hated rich people.

I destroyed their cars because I was jealous of their fancy lives. They had something I did not have. That time I stole the medicine from the pharmacy, I didn't do it because I wanted it. I took the medicine because I had to.

Because of my ill mother. I tried to help.

At the motel, I did not decide to start my own business because I wanted to do it. I started my own business because I let the desires of other people decide for me. Then in Miami, after three days on the bus, the lady did not tell me the most painful words I ever heard because she wanted to hurt me. The lady said those things because she wanted to tell me the truth. Then in …

We cannot afford to think like this. Be happy with what you have. Do what other people your age are doing. Stop dreaming. You can never do it. Do not think it over, sit in front of the TV. This is not the life for you. Find yourself a regular job. When will you finally be an adult. Money spoils people. You're not …

There have been many other convictions I have taken from my parents, from television, or from the other people around me. Suddenly I felt a sense of extreme relief. The burden I was been carrying all these years had gone away. I was free.

Meanwhile, as I was asking myself, why did I realize it only now, why did it take so long, John had come back. Without hesitation, he got straight to the point.

How do you feel now, Tom?

Great, John. It's like a miracle. I did not know what writing could do for somebody. I'm very happy.

Please give me the paper where you wrote down all your negatives.

When I handed it to him, he took out a lighter from his bag and lit it. Then he looked at me and shared these words:

This piece of paper, along with what was written on it, does not mean anything. Forget it. Your mind is now clean.

There was only one paper on the table. I had no idea what to do.

Stand in front of this mirror. John asked me to do so. I listened to him. I stood in front of the mirror with the paper in hand. Totally confused.

Read what you wrote.

I finished primary school.

I added twenty-two pounds to my Bench Press.

I survived winter on the street.

I found a job. I sold my drawings.

I passed my driving license.

They wrote about me in the newspaper.

They accepted me for an internship.

I learned to cook.

I ... *Louder!*

I finished primary school.

I added twenty-two pounds to my Bench Press.

I survived winter on the street.

I ... *Again. Louder!*

I finished primary school.

I added twenty-two pounds to my Bench Press.

I ...

I looked at myself like I was a winner. I felt in myself such incredible self-confidence, determination, motivation, pleasure, strength, energy, and the desire to achieve great things. Hungry after success ...

You should remember this day, Tom! You revealed an infinite power in yourself. This piece of paper with your successes is your ticket to the top. Reading this paper will give you the power to continue when other people have long given up. This paper gives you the reasons to believe in yourself when other people would long believe in somebody else.

Every single success you achieved, write it on this paper. No matter how big the success you have achieved, you just write it down. Did you add four pounds of muscle mass? Super! Write it down. Have you bought your first car? Super! Write it down. Did you negotiate a discount from a salesman? Super! Write it down. You preferred to work before sleep? Super! Write it down. You understand?

Yes, John, I know.

Every morning after you wake up, stand in front of the mirror and read aloud all your achievements. Every morning of your life.

Just do not forget! Reading books, affirmations, visualizing, meditation – these are essential. But actually practicing these things will not make you succeed. Hard work doing the right things is the most important thing. It is a necessity for success.

Our conversation was interrupted by John's ringing phone. When he finished the call, he apologized. He had to fly to London immediately to buy the property for his next recording studio.

A few minutes later I received an SMS from John. Again, he excused himself for not being able to spend more time with me. He also wrote:

Repeat these words at least twice a day, but you really have to believe them. Only then it will work.

I am successful.

I'm somebody.

I'm important.

I overcome my fears.

I'm healthy, happy, and I feel fantastic.

I am more than it seems, all the power of the world is in me.

I am the best.

I'm the best architect in Los Angeles.

Simple words, such huge power. John was not just my boss. He became my friend, my mentor.

No more complaints. No more worries. No more sorrow. No more blame.

No more excuses. No more envy.

No more assumptions. No more hesitation.

No more wasting time. No more boredom.

No more procrastination. No more depression.

No more fear. No more comparing.

No more comfort. No more laziness.

No more despair.

I am a new person.

A better person. A stronger person. The world does not owe me anything. I owe it to myself to fulfill my potential, to share the talent I was born with.

My life, my future is in my hands.

My parents who brought me into this world gave me a roof over my head and the basic things I needed to survive during my childhood.

My parents were also my teachers. They taught me how to behave, how to think, how to act, how to live life. Everything they did, I did the same. That's why I was who I was.

A victim.

Now I have new teachers. Rich, successful, and happy.

I do what they do.

I do what they do.

I know that soon enough, I will belong among them as well. Among the extraordinary people with extraordinary lives.

They had chosen me as one of the thirty-seven.

Those thirty-six applicants had titles from the most prestigious universities in America, and yet they chose me.

A street artist with his wooden stand. The beginning was difficult, but I did not give up. My patience, my passion, my efforts, my talents and hard work moved me further. Everyday I improved. Two months after my start as a trainee, I was achieving the same results as some of the full-time employees who had been with the company for five years.

I was not one of those cute trainees who serves the others coffee or shreds unnecessary papers. I belonged as one of the honorable members of their elite team. I shared every single project that this company received with them. Everything I touched I turned to gold. Literally.

Among my colleagues, I was one of the most popular. Among the clients, I belonged among the most demanding. Among the architects, I belonged to the best.

All those days I spent drawing on a dirty street had developed my talent, my skills. As a trainee, I achieved extraordinary results. As a street artist I achieved incredible results. I did not need any more proof. I found a place where I really belong. I can look at anyone directly in the eyes and say honestly to them:

I do my job because I want to and I love it.

I originally planned to complete the internship and then choose my own path. From the planned six months of internship, another twenty-one months of work started, and I became a full-time architect.

I stopped working at John's recording studio.

I stopped drawing at the beach by the stall. I almost stopped reading all the "wise" books. I spent most of my time in my office drawing up houses, hotels, and skyscrapers. The time at my job passed extremely quickly. In the morning I sat down in the office chair, and a little later I was having dinner at my table.

Outside of work, I spent Saturdays with John together with his wife. I enjoyed Sundays with my girlfriend. By coincidence we met at my work. She worked for a very wealthy Canadian investor as his executive assistant. She brought me the draft of a new skyscraper project. When I saw her, I knew it had to be her.

That's right. Without hesitation, I invited her on that day for dinner. She agreed. And we've been together ever since.

Besides love, it brings us something else. Our struggles. We both grew up in a similar environment. We both tasted the bitter taste of the street. We were both warriors. We both had gotten to the bottom before we found out who we really are.

Thanks to this, I discovered romance in myself. Dinner at good restaurants with orange juice and red roses, with night walks along the beach observing the night sky, has become our regular routine.

Right now I'm living the happiest and most beautiful period of my life.

I have a loving girlfriend.

I have good friends.

I do the work I love.

Every time I am at the beach, I remember the time I was standing with my burned skin next to that ice cream stall drawing what people asked me. Basically, I'm doing the same now. I still draw what people ask for, with only one difference. I draw in a totally different place. Just like John told me.

Surprisingly, he also supported my career as an employee. But he warned me of the pitfalls that threaten those who work for someone else for too long. He consistently explained to me that working for other people, where I am not my own boss, leads to becoming dependent on the feelings of security, regularity, the commands of others, and I would lose the courage to take risks.

For a long time I thought about John's words. They made sense to me. I am regularly rewarded as the best architect in the company.

I have my own office.

I even have my own assistant.

Every time I get the most important projects.

I think that if I continue to work for this company,

I will not move further. I have nothing more to achieve. As an architect, I have reached the top in this company. There is no way to overcome my previous results. I do not want to be one of those people who are satisfied with their results, doing the same job in the same place for the rest of their lives. I cannot do that. I cannot be like them. Dependent on the feelings of certainty. On orders from other people.

It's true. My courage to take risks was almost gone. I got used to being a regular employee. Managed by someone else's orders. Work from Monday to Friday.

It's time to change! I want to be one of those people who achieve ever greater and greater achievements.

They overcome their limits. Moving forward, not backward.

There was only one way to do that: to open up my own architectural studio as I planned two years ago.

What I needed to learn, I learned.

What I needed to see, I saw.

What I needed to hear, I heard.

I have experience.

I have a portfolio.

I have recommendations.

I have everything I need to open my own studio.

I will not wait for the right conditions at the right time, I'll do it right now!

This time I did not need books titled" How to open my own architectural studio," or "how to build a million-dollar worth architectural studio."I could rely only on myself.

At work, I informed my boss and my colleagues about my decision to leave. They did not take it too enthusiastically. They tried to convince me, to deter me.

Without any success, as I did not listen to them. I covered my ears and continued on. This is my life! I will do what I want to do and not what other people want me to do! Those times are long over me. I have only one life. So why should I throw it away by fulfilling the dreams of other people?

I know who I am.

I know what I am extraordinary at.

I know what I want.

And I am living my dream.

It does not matter how many obstacles I have to overcome.

It does not matter how many things I have to sacrifice. Nothing can stop me. Nothing can break me.

My dreams will become a reality.

I did not leave my office as a loser. I was leaving as a prized winner. I was leaving the old place where I achieved great things, but now I was coming to a new place where I can achieve unbelievable things.

When the gossip about my resignation from the company spread out, I started to receive a job offers from other architectural firms. Not just from American companies. I also received offers from Asia, Australia, France. Even from Dubai. These companies did not set up a salary for me. I was the one who was supposed to determine the amount of my salary. I rejected them politely, but I was pleased. It pleased me because it was proof that the twenty-nine months spent gaining experience, working for some-one else was worth it. I had built up an excellent reputation. The name Tom Seed meant something in this field.

In my 25 years on Earth, I had set up my own architectural studio. With this decision, I was risking everything. I left the work where I belonged as one of the best architects with a regular monthly salary. With fixed working hours.

I burned all the bridges behind me. There was no way back.

I did not regret it. I had made the right decision.

Since I opened my own studio, my life changed drastically. I live a completely different life.

A better life.

A richer life.

I am my own boss, guided by my own rules.

I come in when I want to.

I work when I want.

I do things the way I want.

I have more time than ever before.

I have more freedom than ever before.

I earn more money than ever before.

I do not need any certainty.

My life is in my hands, because I know that tomorrow depends on my today.

Best of all, I do not ask people for new projects. People from all over the world are asking me to work on their projects.

I am not asking anymore, I am asked.

Even though I am already on the side of the winners, I do not forget about those who are not.

After six years I returned to New York to visit my mother's grave for the first time. I brought her a beautiful bouquet of flowers. I had not forgotten her.

I thanked her for bringing me to this world. Without her I would not be here.

I love you, mom. I miss you.

In this city, I needed to visit another woman. A woman who deserves my apology. I bought her red roses, and I went with them to the pharmacy. The same woman was standing there as six years ago. She had not changed at all. I waited for the last customer to leave.

Then I approached her with the words: maybe you remember me and maybe not, but a few years ago I stood here just like I'm standing here now. At that time, I did a thing that I still feel ashamed of. Without paying, I stole your medicine and ran away with it as a thief. I'm sorry...

She did not care about my apology. She asked me to leave the pharmacy. I fully understood it. I put the red roses on the counter. I believe she enjoyed them more than my presence.

After returning to Los Angeles, I bought three bouquets of flowers for my dear friends, Mike,

Bill and Double M. It was my honor to meet you.

I miss you. I sat down on the ground beside the gravestones and remembered the moments we spent together. Thank you. Without you I would have never started drawing on the street. Without you, I could not do what I did. Thank you, guys.

So many times before I had failed, but thanks to my previous failures, I found out who I really am and what I am extraordinary at.

I found the meaning of my life. I was born to draw.

I have been experiencing success since

I decided to focus all my energy, all my time, on only one thing. Drawing.

I started out on a dirty street. The place where other people end their lives. But my life just started there. I had sacrificed almost two years of my life, gaining the experience needed to open my own architectural studio, and thanks to this I have achieved freedom for the rest of my life.

All my life I was looking for success around me. But all that time, success was hidden inside me. I was so blinded by looking around myself that I forgot to look into the inner me …

Praise will please me. Critique will change me.
It changes me for good or bad.
It moves me forward or drags me down.

Please, share your opinion. The honest opinion that
is shared with you by your inner voice.
Write a review on Amazon, Goodreads …
Upload a photo on Instagram …
Create a YouTube review …
Recommend the book to your friends, even if they're only
Facebook friends …

Every little thing matters.
Positive feedback, constructive feedback.
Just tell the truth.

Do you like my book? Do you hate my book?
Was it an eye opener for you?
Was it beneficial for you?
Have you read something much better?
Was it worth the money?
Any advice for me?

Show your emotions.

I put my heart into this book.
I ask you to do the same.

Tag your photo with the
#beforeiwon #tomasveres
hashtag

Please feel free to contact me at any time.
tomasveres.com/contact

~~BEFORE I WON~~
BEFORE I FAILED

ISBN 978-80-973115-0-6

Made in the USA
Middletown, DE
23 December 2021

56933958R00084